No Need for Weed

Understanding and Breaking
Cannabis Dependency

James Langton

In association with Clearhead

Published 2008 by Hindsight Press

© James Langton 2008

All rights reserved

ISBN 978-0-9557626-0-4

Hindsight Press, The Meridian, 4 Copthall House, Station Square, Coventry, CV1 2FL

The information in this book is based on the personal and professional experiences of the author it is not intended as a substitute for consulting with your doctor or health-care provider. Hindsight press and the author are not responsible for any adverse effects or consequeneces resulting directly or indirectly from the use of any of the suggestions discussed in this book. All matters pertaining to your individual health should be supervised by a health care professional.

Printed in the United Kingdom by Lightning Source Ltd

James Langton: "When I was smoking cannabis it was the most important relationship in my life: more important than my family, my friends, my partner or my job. I smoked it to help me wake up and to help me get to sleep. When I was without it I was irritable, anxious and could concentrate on little else until I was stoned again. However, if you had asked me at any time whether I was addicted, I would have laughed in your face and denied it. I finally found the strength to quit in 2002."

James Langton founded **Clearhead** as a support website in 2004 and, with his colleague Adrienne MacLeod, started running weekend workshops on cannabis addiction in 2005. He lives and works in London, England.

"Things are going well for me... Still smoke free and generally feeling marvellously liberated from my previous regime of endlessly smoking joints. I found the book tremendously useful, I can't really stress this enough, and was gripped from the very first paragraph... The section about confidence, previous failure and crucially acceptance were invaluable, as I'd tried to stop before and 'failed'. But I had done this without any kind of analysis... The part on anger also really struck a chord, although funnily enough I now find my moods to be much more stable and handle things a lot better - I really believed weed helped me deal with things when in fact I now see that wasn't really the case at all. Caroline - London 2007*

Contents

Section 1 Early Days

Section 2 Stoned Perspective

Section 3 Starting to Stop

Section 4 Adjustment

Section 5 Recovery

Acknowledgements

Adrienne and myself are sincerely grateful to every single attendee of our Clearhead workshops in London. It goes without saying we learnt at least as much from all of you as you did from us – probably more. Without your input this book could never have been written.

Also, thank-you to the many people who have posted messages on the Clearhead boards over the last few years. Your honesty and willingness to share your struggles with cannabis addiction is an ongoing inspiration.

I would also like to thank all the people at the Marijuana Anonymous Fellowship in London who supported me when I needed it. Especially Jo, Adam, Sarah, Megan from Clapham, Dave in Brooklyn and Carol in Los Angeles, who became my friends. Thank-you also to Tim S. who taught me how to email and helped get the show on the road.

Thanks also to Dick, the great enabler; Rachel, Mark and Graham the editors; and all my extended family for not judging me too harshly.

Finally, thank-you to Clare, Mike, and Rowan for your stories, as well as to Jeanette, for the before and after, and DHR for the laughs along the way.

The personal information in the client scenarios that I have included has been altered in order to ensure confidentiality. All names, identifying information and other factors have been changed. Many of the stories are composite sketches. Any resemblance you may find between a story and someone you know is purely coincidental.

This book is dedicated to my colleague Adrienne MacLeod: your insight and energy cleared my head so many times when I needed it most.

James Langton 2007

Preface

Cannabis Gran sentenced

A grandmother who extols the virtue of cooking with cannabis has been sentenced to 250 hours community service after being convicted of illegally growing the drug at her home.

Patricia Tabram, 68, a former chef from Humshaugh, Northumberland, told the court that she used the drug to ease her depression, as well as her aches and pains. But she now faces being evicted from her housing association bungalow after a jury at Carlisle Crown Court found her guilty of cultivation and possession of the class C drug.

Judge Barbara Forrester told the grey-haired pensioner yesterday that she must pay £1,000 costs as well as carry out 175 hours of community service for cultivating four cannabis plants, and a further 75 hours for possessing powdered cannabis which she stored in her kitchen and added to cakes, curries, casseroles and soups.

Tabram was unbowed after the case, insisting she would defy the law and continue to take cannabis. Tabram has for many years campaigned for the legalization of cannabis, appearing on television shows as well as writing a book entitled Grandma Eats Cannabis. At the 2005 general election she stood, unsuccessfully, against the cabinet minister Peter Hain on a pro-cannabis ticket.

In May 2004 she was caught with 31 plants and blocks of cannabis worth

£850 at her home which she used to make dishes for the elderly and infirm people in her area.

She used it to relieve depression since finding her fourteen-year-old son Duncan dead in bed in 1975. She also claimed eating the drug helped combat aches and pains she suffered as a result of two car crashes.

When asked before her sentence whether she feared going to jail, Tabram, who used to run a restaurant in Leith, Edinburgh, said, "Emmeline Pankhurst had to go to prison three times before women got the vote, so I am not going to be worried about it."

(Newspaper report, March 2007)

Saturday 10 March 2007 1 a.m.

In a few hours' time I'll be running a Clearhead workshop to help a small group of people come to terms with their dependence on cannabis. My colleague, Adrienne, and I have been running these workshops for about 18 months now, and I always feel slightly nervous the night before, curious about what sort of people are going to show and whether we will be able to give them the best possible advice and support. So far we've been incredibly lucky. Almost every single person we've worked with has been … well, just nice. Typical dope smokers, really; ordinary people for whom a happy habit has slipped out of control.

One thing I do know as I go to bed and try to relax before

sleeping is that all the participants next morning will be a lot more nervous than I am. I have been in email contact with some of them for months as they agonize over whether they really do have a problem with weed. Most have been smoking since they were school age, and the idea of saying goodbye to a drug they have treated as a best friend for so many years is almost always a frightening prospect.

To help turn off my mind, I listen to the radio for a while before sleeping. While channel surfing I come across a phone-in show and am plugged straight into a heated debate between Cannabis Gran Pat Tabram and the current contender for dope prohibitionist of the year, the Reverend George Hargreaves. Poor George is getting crucified, not only by Pat but also by caller after caller. He's not doing himself any favours, however, as he has a certain self-righteous indignation that doesn't play well with the listeners.

Pat comes over as an archetypal grandmother, although sometimes when she talks about cannabis she sounds just like any 17-year-old stoner, still hopelessly in love with the stuff. Eventually, after maybe the fifth or sixth caller telling George how they use dope to help with a variety of injuries and illnesses, or simply to relax after a hard day at work, he finally begins to understand that simply saying cannabis is the 'devil's drug' is not going to win him this debate.

To be fair to George, I read his story in *The Daily Mail* a few weeks ago, in which he wrote about his son's chaotic relationship with skunk, which over a period of time led to some serious mental health problems and a suicide attempt. But tonight he's been KO'd by the Cannabis Gran.

Introduction

'The future ain't what it used to be.'
Yogi Berra, American baseball star/manager

When I tell people I work for a programme that helps people who want to stop smoking cannabis, the reaction I get is invariably along the lines of, "Why do you want to make people stop? What's wrong with smoking a bit of weed?" Or simply, "I didn't think it was addictive." And it is true there are many people who start smoking when teenagers or in their early 20s, perhaps smoking quite heavily for a number of years, who, when they feel ready to, are able to give it up quite easily. Also, many users believe that, compared to alcohol, nicotine and harder drugs, the health risks from smoking dope are trivial to non-existent.

I am not a hypocrite. I smoked cannabis heavily myself for many years; sometimes quite happily, at other times less so. I had many good times when smoking, especially in the early days. But there came a point, about five years before I finally quit, when I decided that I wanted to stop. I had tried:
- Cutting down.
- Only smoking on weekends.
- Not buying any weed, just sharing joints with others.
- Leaving my stash with distant family members.
- Impulsive/desperate cold turkey.

Many times I would throw my bag of dope away before going to bed, only to be rooting through my dustbin the following morning. And yet I still didn't admit to myself that I was addicted. How could I be dependent on something that was only *psychologically* addictive? A drug that, compared to all I knew about heroin addiction or alcoholism, was not supposed to have any withdrawal symptoms.

Yet in the last few years there have been remarkable changes in the scientific study of addiction. Today there are support groups for addiction to food, gambling, emotional spending, and even compulsive sex. Addiction is no longer exclusively linked to the chemical structure of an opiate. I now understand the power of psychological addiction. There is no hierarchy when it comes to addiction. Although there may be differences in the physical symptoms of withdrawal, there is no difference in terms of psychological dependence to cannabis or any other drug or behaviour.

In fact, the emotional bond may be stronger with dope because smoking a joint is for many of us our first mood-altering chemical experience. I see now that I never allowed myself to go anywhere near withdrawal, psychological or otherwise. Over a 30-year period, I could count the days when I didn't get my cannabis fix, barely reaching double figures.

Quitting cannabis is not like quitting cigarettes, although there are of course features common to breaking any habit or addiction. If you were to offer almost any cigarette smoker the opportunity to go back in time to the point where they accepted their first cigarette, almost all would jump at the chance to turn the clock back, knowing what they know now about the reality of nicotine addiction.

Cigarette smoking offers very few plus points – it doesn't change your mood, it's not socially acceptable, and it cannot in all honesty be described as a fun activity. Cannabis, on the other hand, is undeniably a mood-changing drug. Today, it's probably more socially acceptable in many ways to admit to being a pot user rather than a cigarette smoker, or even a heavy drinker; and yes, in the right circumstances, smoking dope to get high can be a lot of fun.

So why quit cannabis? For me personally, I found the focus of my life had narrowed to the point where my obsession with weed meant that I was moving further and further away from things I still wanted to achieve. My existence had become a vicious circle of inaction. I smoked to forget how small my world had become, which in itself was due not only to how much weed I was consuming every day but also the importance I placed on needing to have my supply secure in order to feel safe.

Different people decide to address their dope smoking for a

variety of reasons. Numerous people contact Clearhead because their cannabis habit is damaging their relationships, or they find it's affecting their memory and concentration. Some find they have become isolated from friends and family, or maybe the side-effects leave them paranoid, depressed, or anxious when they smoke. Others have the self-knowledge to recognise that they are smoking to cover up uncomfortable feelings and emotions.

Many have stepped out of denial and simply accept that they are addicted and want to regain a sense of freedom. Often there are practical problems of debt, unfinished college work, or employment slippage. Almost all dope smokers worry about the damage they are inflicting on their heart, lungs and respiratory system; and of course, the increased risk of developing cancer.

The fact is that, globally, cannabis is the second most widely used mood-altering drug after alcohol. In most societies its presence is almost totally mainstream, regardless of prohibition or legality. Tens of millions of people smoke it every day, and it would be unrealistic to think that all cannabis smokers are happy smokers, and that nobody has problems when they try and quit, or even when they just want to take a break for a while.

Rational drug and alcohol commentators today accept that cannabis legality is not the only issue. They recognize that much more work needs to be done on educating both young people and experienced users not only about the potential associated risks to mental and physical health but, just as importantly, how easy it is to become reliant on a drug broadly considered non-habit forming.

So many people I meet who smoke dope obsessively would love to be in a position where they could control their use again like they did during their early years of getting high. Although they recognize the negative effects of overuse, they can't imagine quitting completely because there are still elements of enjoyment.

Problems occur if, as with all potentially addictive substances and behaviours, you have the sort of character or genetic makeup that means you find it difficult stopping yourself over-doing the things you enjoy. It's as if the brain lacks the critical on/off valve that warns us our lack of control is becoming extreme and is interfering with other areas of our life.

Denial and addiction go hand in hand. Your mind can always find excuses, assuring you that your relationship with cannabis is normal, a reward, an essential aid to sleep, or something you just can't relax without. Possibly you believe it to be a tool that you *need* to function creatively. At Clearhead, we see another, more simple aspect of denial when some participants come to our workshops and are stunned as they realize just how much of their monthly income is spent on weed.

Clearhead is primarily a non-judgemental support programme. If you feel that you are a happy toker and that any negative consequences from your cannabis smoking are acceptable, then we respect your decision; but we also consider that when somebody decides to quit, or even becomes curious as to what their life might be like without using or obsessing about cannabis every day, then there should be specialized advice and help available to support them.

For most cannabis smokers the idea of stopping forever is quite literally terrifying. Some see clearly how their fixation keeps them stuck, but their emotional ties with the drug are so powerful that the fear of letting go is stronger than the motivation for positive change.

Perhaps you would like to take a break from cannabis or be in more control of your smoking. Certainly the idea of this book is to help you break your dependence, your reliance on getting stoned just to get you through the days or nights of your life, but maybe the idea of stopping even for a short while seems impossible.

- Because getting stoned is what you do.
- Because sometimes it feels as if it's what you've always done.

- Because you can't remember a time when you didn't smoke dope.
- Because you've smoked since you were a teenager, without discrimination, without question.

As you read on you will understand more about why you use cannabis, and perhaps you will begin to see, like I eventually did, that for some people, the longer they smoke, the more the returns diminish.

Hard as governments and law enforcement agencies try, nobody can really force you to stop smoking dope. They can put you in prison but, even then, we all know that prison is not necessarily the drug-free environment it's supposed to be. They can tighten up on the dealer networks, but it's simple enough to have a few plants growing somewhere around your home for your own personal use.

This book is designed to let you consider your relationship with dope openly and honestly, and then allow you to begin to make some profound choices as to whether cannabis really adds anything to the quality of your life anymore.

Many dope smokers, perhaps the majority, are happy to use cannabis every day, but one definition of dependence is: *The compulsive use of a substance, or behaviour, to the point where we have no effective choice but continued use despite negative consequences.*

'Negative consequences', that's the big one, and *most* cannabis smokers find that *most* of the time their lives function reasonably well. But everyday cannabis smoking has a way of keeping us stuck, of subtly stopping us getting more out of life. It's just so much easier to smoke a joint than to do … well, almost anything else. Coming from that perspective, my experience was that after six months of abstinence, I made the amazing discovery that I didn't miss it at all. I appreciated the extra energy, the clarity of thought, my new-found confidence, the lack of paranoia, my sociability, and a sense of well-being that I genuinely hadn't experienced for years. My truth is that although I smoked cannabis obsessively for 30 years, I probably got all that I needed from it after about five. I just didn't want to go through the withdrawal process or leave behind something that had been central to my life since my early teens.

To repeat. Almost all habitual smokers are fearful of the withdrawal, but for some people the whole process is surprisingly easy; for others it can be a real challenge getting through the first few weeks. This book can be used as a manual to make your progress as painless as possible, by signposting what to expect and how to roll with the punches and come out the other side free of dependence and open to what your new life may have in store for you.

You might want to be more in control of your smoking rather than stop completely. I'm afraid the reality is that most people need to make an initial clean break, for a significant period of time. It takes about three weeks to break the habit, for your mind to adjust to the fact that you're not smoking anymore. It takes up to six weeks for the last traces of cannabis to physically leave your body. If you can go three months without picking up a joint, I can almost guarantee that you will be feeling better physically, mentally and emotionally than you have done for years. After six months dope-free, you may be in a position where you can make decisions about whether you want to start smoking again, and if you could control your intake if you did.

If you have ever tried to cut down your consumption yourself, after being used to smoking every day, you will know that it's very, very difficult to limit yourself to just weekends, or in some cases just one or two joints a night. For someone like myself, who smoked every morning and then carried on through the day, to be able to cut down to just smoking in the evenings would have been a real achievement, and I *just* couldn't do it on my own. I had no one to turn to for support when I went through my own long period of failed attempts and broken promises to myself and others. Ultimately, I forced myself to quit by going on a ten-day silent meditation retreat to break the habit, and then found caring, ongoing support from Marijuana Anonymous in London.

Perhaps you don't feel ready to stop immediately. The early

chapters of this book will allow you to begin to analyse your relationship with weed, right up to the *Starting to Stop* section, which, if used correctly, will help you become super-conscious of every joint you smoke. This will enable you to begin to judge what you are actually getting out of your habit, and to balance this with what it is taking from you. Sometimes we have to experiment with abstinence, just as we experimented with getting high during our early years of smoking.

It's up to you now, as you read this introduction, to decide whether you want to read further. You can think about what you've read so far to help you decide if you're really still a happy smoker or whether the drug is taking more from you than it gives back. It's likely you have been smoking since your teenage years, perhaps even earlier. If you do *anything* every day, be it positive or negative, from that early an age, then the ritual, the habit, will become part of you.

However, this doesn't mean to say it has to be a part of you forever. Life is a journey, a path, and it constantly shifts under our own direction. It may seem like we're not moving forward in our lives, but time passes. Whether you have been smoking for 5, 10, 20 or 30 years, it's never too late for positive change; and the truth is that when you finally decide to have a go at living with a clear head, you will see that the one thing you believed you couldn't live without is actually far less significant than you had thought.

The structure of this book

The book is divided into five sections. **The first section** looks at the early days of smoking – why we might have started to use cannabis in the first place, how it can stunt emotional growth, how it can become the focus of identity, and how extended use can gradually accelerate to the point where it can begin to control our life.

The second section examines life from a stoned perspective, demonstrating how the ordinary day-to-day stuff can become more and more difficult as prolonged cannabis use begins to limit our choices and our potential. For some people, a stoned perspective can involve a dark journey of paranoia, anxiety and depression.

I analyse the holy trinity of cannabis, alcohol and tobacco, and particularly how long-term cannabis use can slowly bring us to the point where we rely on weed just to keep going. I also explore how continuous overuse keeps us stuck in a destructive cycle of procrastination, and how what was once a pleasurable experience can for some turn into an obsession and ultimately a trap.

The third section offers a step-by-step guide to quitting, using both my own experience and the success stories of some of the other people who I have worked with and who have also finally managed to make the break from cannabis and move on. This part of the book has been designed to offer guidance, support and positive reinforcement to help prepare you in the most effective way possible for a journey to a healthier lifestyle, free of cannabis dependence.

The fourth section is written to help the reader through the adjustment period – those first few critical weeks as the mind and body adjust to their new situation. Feelings and emotions begin to re-awaken, which can result in unpredictable fluctuations of physical and emotional energy.

The fifth section takes the reader forward into long-term recovery, to help you find the strength and support that will allow you to keep advancing and make the most of this positive life-change, in which you will get so much more from life than struggling through a daily fog of low energy and indecision.

Clearhead hypnotherapy recording

The idea of change, even positive change can often be daunting and so Clearhead and hypnotherapist Angela Jullings have produced a powerful hypnotherapy recording that can be used in conjunction with this book. The recording offers a rapid effective route to deep natural relaxation, and is especially useful if you have concerns about cannabis and your sleeping pattern.

For further information about Angela, and how to purchase this recording please turn to page 223.

Do I have a problem with cannabis?

You might want to consider these questions. It's not a test but when I was smoking some of these made me stop and think, and eventually think and stop.

Is cannabis your primary, or only way of relaxing?

Are you using cannabis to suppress uncomfortable feelings and emotions?

Are you consistently trying and failing to cut down or stop smoking cannabis?

Do you mainly smoke by yourself?

Do you often feel disconnected from life?

Are you smoking cannabis to avoid dealing with problems?

Are you smoking cannabis to avoid dealing with life?

Do you still enjoy smoking cannabis?

Section 1 Early Days

1. First Love

They say every alcoholic remembers their first drink, and of course it's just as true, perhaps more so, that everybody who ever fell in love with smoking dope will also have a vivid memory of their first joint and discovering for themselves what getting high was all about.

Most people's teenage experiences with illicit cannabis smoking will be linked with excitement, adventure and friendship. Maybe clubbing together once a week with your mates to score an eighth for the weekend; perhaps it was a shared joint with your best friend after school; or possibly a fragment or two stolen from your big brother's stash box to take to a party on a Saturday night.

How can you describe what it feels like to get high, really high, to someone who has never experienced it? I'm not sure that I can. A release of pressure, an increased sensitivity, a freeing of the imagination, an almost imperceptible bending of consciousness, a near dreamlike state, a physical feeling of warmth like being wrapped up in a blanket. Perhaps some of these things, possibly none. Everybody will have their own personal experience.

Some of us, however, may have been driven by a darker

need, perhaps at a painfully young age, to seek out what we instinctively knew would offer us relief from feelings and inadequacies that couldn't be understood, let alone articulated, at the time. Then again, one or two of the most hard-core dope smokers to have passed through our Clearhead workshops made a point of staying away from weed all though their teenage years, and even through their 20s, but at some point decided it couldn't do them any harm just to try it and see what all the fuss was about.

A large proportion of the population, of course, have never smoked dope, or maybe did so just once and found that it wasn't for them. Perhaps for these people it was the idea of putting any kind of smoke into their lungs that put them off, or possibly the only result from taking a few tokes on a joint was to feel dizzy or sick.

This book, however, is dedicated to experienced smokers, for those like myself who at some time – perhaps many times – said to themselves that discovering dope was the best thing that ever happened to them, who fell blindly in love with the drug, in all its forms, without a second thought. But this book is also for those who, just like me, found that ending this love affair was much more difficult than they could ever have imagined when they smoked their first joint and got high for the very first time.

2. Mistaken Identity

'We are what we repeatedly do.'

Aristotle

When I started smoking in my teens, the fact that cannabis was part of a wider illegal drug culture chimed perfectly with the rebellious side of my personality. In the 60s and 70s it was quite possible to get arrested and put in prison just for possession of a few grams of hash. The risk was part of the lifestyle, and it was important to me that those I considered my real friends were also dope smokers. Admittedly this was partly to make sure that I always had a continual supply, but also because I sincerely believed that only others exposed to cannabis and the drug culture would share my philosophy and world view.

These days things have changed, simply because of scale of use. Today smoking weed openly on the street barely registers, either with the police or with many of the community at large. It's not clever to be caught literally smoking in front of the law, but beyond that, weed is often just a fact of life. In some families dope is tolerated by parents as the price they pay for their children's compliance.

The authorities may not want to hear this, but cannabis has become almost totally conventional. The way people identify with dope has changed, not just since the 2002 reclassification here in the UK but for a decade or more now; and certainly for a significant number of people, including some of the very young, smoking a joint is just as normal as enjoying a can of beer or a cup of tea. There are some, of course, who without realizing it use dope as medicine, pure and simple. Keeping their emotions in check, screening out the worst and more painful aspects of their lives. Many have enough insight to accept that they are addicted. There is now growing evidence to suggest that a few young people are criminalized at an early age and begin to steal or even deal harder drugs to feed their addiction.

I think it's fair to say that almost anybody who smokes dope heavily has invested at least part of their identity in their favourite hobby. As the ritual act of rolling and smoking joints becomes no more than a reflex, just part of a daily routine, how could it be any other way? It's just what we do, and so to some extent it also becomes who we are.

As we progress through life, some of our deeply held feelings and opinions concerning our right to smoke weed might have been saved up from adolescence; these may have hardened as we become more detached from other aspects of everyday living. When I was smoking, my personal relationship with cannabis had become more important to me than almost any other. After a while, dope did nothing to make me feel better about myself. Eventually it took over my identity, and for most of my years of smoking I saw myself as somehow detached from much of the rest of society. It became too easy to divide my world into those who I felt understood the drug culture and those I judged would never in a million years understand that, yes, as well as being dangerous, illegal substances can help you feel differently about life in a positive way.

One of my fears about quitting was that I would lose out on the social aspect of sharing a joint. The truth for me, however, was that by the time I got round to putting away my stash box, I had very few friends and acquaintances left to worry about. Most of my older friends had stopped smoking years ago, and the common factor that I shared with my few remaining dope-smoking buddies was how cut off we had become. Sure, we used to sit around and smoke together, but apart from that, I seemed to hide away from so many other social opportunities, probably because after years of smoking I could no longer trust myself to be even half-way coherent when I was stoned.

As modern life relentlessly takes away the drive toward social interaction, it becomes ever easier to cut ourselves off from our communities, our neighbours, even our own families. Smoking dope can seem the perfect way to keep ourselves from being bored with our own company. If we use alcohol and other drugs to boost our confidence, surely it must be okay to smoke weed when we want to relax. The problem is it's just so easy to go beyond relaxation and into isolation.

I'm sure that most dedicated dope smokers will have at some point fantasized that if cannabis rather than alcohol was society's drug of choice then the world would be a happier, possibly a safer, place. How many potheads haven't at one time or another ranted and raved about drug laws that criminalize what is essentially a pastime that harms no one but the user himself.

Many people become politically active on this issue because they see their weed smoking as their only illegal activity. They also point to the perceived medical benefits of pot. "How can it be fair," they ask, "to deny people in chronic pain the relief of using cannabis, a plant that has been taken as medicine by the sick for thousands of years?" They may well be right, but I remember when I first heard about licensed cannabis clinics in California, my immediate thought was that it was a scam. I fantasized about moving to America and pretending to be sick, just to secure my particular *medicine* of choice on prescription.

As society as a whole becomes more aware about some of the very real potential dangers from cannabis overuse and, conversely, generally more attracted to the benefits of a healthier lifestyle, I'm personally less interested in the freedom to smoke dope (people will always find a way), and more concerned about how to live life with the continued optimum health I am now lucky enough to possess. I would argue, although only from my own personal experience, that dope smoking kept in place a predominantly unhealthy lifestyle. My diet was poor, exercise was minimal, my sleep was drugged, the tobacco I was consuming with every joint made my long-term goal of giving up nicotine seem impossible, and any motivation to improve things never got beyond wishful thinking.

It wasn't until I finally quit that I saw that for years weed had robbed me of the energy, confidence and motivation to live life to the full. Long-term dependence meant I'd given in to depression and paranoia, and caused permanent physical damage to myself especially my lungs, and possibly my heart.

Today my self-image has come full circle. My choice of friends and acquaintances is not limited to other smokers. I have the confidence to communicate with all-comers, without feeling that somewhere deep inside I'm living a secret life; and instead of fantasizing about the person I would like to be, I have become him.

3. Protracted Adolescence

Why did you start smoking weed? Was it from curiosity? Perhaps it was to test yourself. Maybe you just wanted to feel that you belonged. I'll bet someone you trusted told you how good it was. Possibly it just seemed the cool thing to do. Or was it you putting two fingers up to every authority figure who ever told you that you shouldn't?

There will, I know, be lots of people reading this who have been brought up in families where smoking weed was the norm, where parents or other adults would share joints with kids because they believed that getting stoned was a relatively harmless pastime. I've met people who were given marijuana tea at an early age by their parents as a method of control, a pacifier.

The 'drug culture' never penetrated my family home. All drugs, apart from alcohol, tobacco and aspirin, were considered mainly a bad thing. Alcohol and tobacco were my mum's drugs of choice; the aspirin was dispensed to us kids as a cure-all when we were sick. So for me, from the first time I saw somebody smoking a joint, on television, I was curious and wanted to try it. I was around 12 years old, and my curiosity probably stemmed from the fact that up to that point I'd lived a relatively sheltered existence. I think I remember seeing a news feature probably designed to warn children my age off drugs, but of course it had the opposite effect.

It took a little while longer before I got the opportunity to satisfy my curiosity, but by the time I was 16 I was well and truly initiated into the drug culture at my school, somehow, from an early age, I sensed that cannabis was going to help me feel better about myself. And it did; it really hit the spot.

Back then, the average age young people discovered weed was around 16, so I was pretty average in that respect; but today it's closer to 14, which means that there are plenty of 11- and 12-year-olds starting their own journey into cannabis culture.

When I was 16 I was **frustrated** and felt I had no control over my life. I was **angry**. I felt permanently misunderstood. I was often **sad and lonely** for reasons I couldn't articulate. I was **confused** as to my identity and what was expected from me. I was **terrified** by the thought of adulthood, which seemed to be just around the corner. This, of course, all adds up to classic adolescent insecurity. The worst thing was I couldn't admit my lack of self-confidence to my friends or even myself. It's hardly surprising that I just wanted to feel good, to smoke dope and to run away from everything that seemed difficult in life. I see all that now, but at the time it just seemed totally natural. Hindsight is, as they say, a wonderful thing.

What do we know of life at 16 years old, let alone at 11, 12 or 14? Looking back at our young selves even a few years later, it seems we could be looking at a completely different person. Were we ever that fearless, that stupid, that brilliant? In our teens, we think we know everything. We almost truly believe that we are invincible and will live forever. For most kids at that age, pot is nothing more than pure fun. It is the thing that bonds friends together, facilitates the possibility of sex, and keeps you cool under pressure.

These days, for most young people, weed is easier to get hold of than booze. Of course it is – your dealer doesn't demand an ID card. The tighter the alcohol laws are enforced and the higher the prices are jacked up, the more teenagers will experiment with street drugs. No wonder kids are smoking dope younger than ever. Here in the UK it's a totally unlicensed market.

Teenagers today have more pressure on them than ever before. Pressure to do well in their exams, pressure to own the coolest stuff, pressure to partner up, pressure to steer clear of bullying and intimidation. In 2005, when 15-year-old school pupils were asked why they *first* took drugs, 79% said they wanted to see what it was like, 30% said they wanted to get high or feel good, whilst only 14% said it was because their friends were doing it. 13% said they wanted to forget their problems. *(Pupils could give more than one answer. Source: Statistics for Drug Misuse Report, England 2007).*

So, contrary to accepted thought, it's not only peer pressure that provokes first use, it's more often curiosity, followed by a stated desire to get high, and for a significant number of young people that means a pull toward a change of emotional landscape. Weed is a part of life for young people; whether taken up or not at school age, it is readily available. Some kids will obviously gravitate towards it. For a few who try it out, there will be the first glimmer of paranoia and anxiety, so they will leave it well alone. But plenty of youngsters will ignore these warning signs because they just enjoy the pleasure they get from being high.

Today there is a greater understanding that smoking cannabis at a young age, for those genetically vulnerable, seriously increases the likelihood of mental health problems either immediately, or down the line. There is growing research evidence that early and regular cannabis smoking can increase the potential for the onset of lifelong psychiatric conditions such as schizophrenia or bipolar disorder; furthermore, there is also an increased risk of developing persistent symptoms of depression and anxiety.

There is one very important aspect of early cannabis use that doesn't get much discussion – it can stunt emotional growth. One of the things all dope smokers love about their drug is that it seems to turn up the volume knob that controls sensory perception. When stoned, we become acutely aware of our environment – how it looks, sounds, smells, or just how it *feels*. Often when entering a place or meeting someone for the first time when we are high, a sort of sixth sense seems to kick in, and we either feel comfortable or uncomfortable, picking up the *vibrations* around us.

But like so much in life, what we gain with one hand we lose with the other. First of all, if you're stoned most of the time (and remember, once dope is in your system it stays there for weeks on end) then you no longer really notice your heightened senses. Everything pretty well feels much the same; and that's a clue. **As your senses are heightened, so your feelings are blunted.** Your feelings are another word for your emotions; and for me, it wasn't until I stopped smoking that I realized to what extent I had been numbing my authentic emotional reality.

Adolescence is the natural time to experience extremes of emotion. Nature gives us this time to go through these hormonal changes, to prepare us, to allow us to test the limits of our emotional range as we enter into adulthood. The problem is that if we're zoning out from these uncomfortable feelings instead of experiencing them, we don't learn how to process them properly. We internalize them. And as we go through our lives screening out these feelings with cannabis, I would argue that on some level we never quite reach the peak of our maturity.

The way so many of us live in this technologically developed age means that, as a society, we have become conditioned to expect everything with immediacy; and although one of the effects of cannabis is that it allows some much-needed perspective on our *'everything, all the time'* lifestyle, there is also a genuine price to pay for this objectivity, and one that is just as subtle.

As teenagers we become used to the extreme instant gratification we get from weed, which means many of us can run in to problems if we try and quit when we get older. We have to re-learn all of our ideas of reality and normality; we have to discover other ways of managing our feelings and our moods. This change requires discipline and a different sort of personal perspective, to allow us to finally reach the end of a protracted adolescence that for the long-term dope smoker can last all the way through to middle-age and beyond.

Section 2 Stoned Perspective

4. Beyond the Pleasure Principle

*'The greatest pleasure in life is in doing what people
say you cannot do.'*
Walter Bagehot, 19th century English social theorist and critic

One reason cannabis is such a popular drug is that it's incredibly versatile; another is that it's clearly habit forming. For the most part, users say they smoke to relax; others accept that it simply makes life less boring, or helps them sleep through the night. It changes consciousness, offering an opportunity to let the mind play freely outside the constrictions of everyday reality.

Many people lead hard-working lives and have little money for entertainment, so they consider a few joints at the end of the day to be just compensation. I have acquaintances that are convinced that if it wasn't for weed they would be even more depressed or unhappy than they already are.

For a long time I was certain that using cannabis was the only way I could get in touch with my creative side, and I have met others who sincerely believed that pot, used as a sacrament, opened a pathway to a spiritual understanding they would never have reached without a relationship with the sacred herb. Some swear they owe cannabis a huge debt, believing that, thanks to its soothing effect, they have managed to break free from a *real* addiction to harder drugs, or that weed has kept them from doing physical harm to themselves or to others.

The arguments for medicinal cannabis use are well known. Anecdotal evidence makes a convincing case for licensed use to help with many conditions, notably for pain relief and for spasm management, as well as respite from the nausea and loss of appetite for those undergoing chemo treatments. Taking these points of view into consideration, it's easy to understand why the pro-cannabis lobby feels resentment over laws that criminalize and threaten their liberty. They might reasonably argue that the nature and uses of cannabis have been long misunderstood by those who never inhaled.

In other words, there is a rational viewpoint that says cannabis, like alcohol, is essentially pretty safe if used appropriately. Many potheads would argue more so. For years I would excuse the massive extent of my smoking by comparing alcohol and cannabis. I would rationalize that, because I would smoke consistently during the day and through the night and consider myself to still be reasonably functional, my use was essentially harmless. I was also convinced that cannabis smoking caused far fewer social problems than alcohol and other drugs.

But it's a question of tolerance and, of course, denial. In the end, I couldn't accept that it was enough to simply be *reasonably* functional. I wanted more from my life.

For a start, I wanted to be clearheaded again; to be able to remember things; to be aware of time passing at normal speed, not stretched or shrunk. I wanted more of a social life. I wanted to be more confident and not so self-obsessed. I wanted to be in control and less lazy. I felt ready to finally grow up and turn away from a pleasure that had evolved into a routine, then into a habit, and finally into full-blown dependency.

Cannabis use, and abuse, has become so politicized that legal considerations leave little room for a real understanding of issues, which go beyond attitudes of pleasure and punishment. At Clearhead, we understand that for many millions, cannabis is for better or worse as much a part of life as eating, drinking, and sleeping.

However it *is* a potentially dangerous drug, certainly there are some very real mental health issues to consider, but also because, contrary to what many people believe, it is addictive, albeit not with great physical intensity, but undoubtedly psychologically. Whilst I'm sure there are worse things to become addicted to, being controlled by any substance or behaviour is a delibitating condition. When that addiction is finally overcome, the onset of free will can be one of the most positive and liberating expressions of human experience. Certainly in my case, better than the dwindling satisfaction I was getting from smoking dope every day.

Perhaps the most contentious strand of the cannabis issue shadows the fact that almost all pot smokers start experimenting in their teens, which is when we are of course vulnerable but also, paradoxically, when we believe ourselves to be almost totally invulnerable. Parents and Government need to finally wise up to the fact that drug education will only be partially effective until it fundamentally challenges children to appreciate and channel their adolescent emotional energies, rather than simply blot them out with weed and alcohol.

Like so many teenagers, cannabis enabled my first real mood-altering experience. Unlike alcohol, I felt I could handle it pretty well. I was 15. Those early experiences of drug initiation were so powerful that they formed part of my identity for a large chunk of my life to follow.

As examined in the last section, school-age cannabis experimentation threatens the still-developing young brain with a significantly increased risk of depression and even schizophrenia in later life. But less is understood about the effect that consistent early-age use has on the neurotransmitters that influence the brain's pleasure and reward system. The psychological impact of teen smoking in terms of gradual dependence is incredibly powerful, but its hold is only fully appreciated when we decide we may want to quit or bring our use under control years later. This can occur when the consistency of our habit begins to interfere with our health or our responsibilities, or simply when we decide that we might want to face some of the emotional issues that we've been hiding from.

Many people who smoke dope long-term are conflicted as to whether their use has become a problem. *"It hasn't stopped me achieving anything I want to achieve." "I hold down a responsible job." "My cannabis smoking doesn't harm anybody else."* Whilst these voices may seem reasonable, there is often an element of panic at the thought of saying goodbye to a parallel existence that may have been a hugely significant part of life for a number of years.

An integral part of understanding addiction is also understanding denial; and it's easy to think that because we smoke weed in the same way as others might enjoy a drink – when we get home from work, for example – that we are not dependent. But whether it's booze or dope, it seems to me that when we begin to use a substance or behaviour to fill **all** the gaps in our lives, to the point where it becomes our primary or only means of relaxation or enjoyment, then it has become a problem. When every other aspect of our lives seems to be refracted through a stoned perspective, this can cause difficulties for us when we try and integrate ourselves more fully into the realities of everyday living.

What worked for us in our teens and early 20s can start to hold us back when we find we are expected to take on more responsibilities as we get older. It's no coincidence that most people who attend our workshops are in their early to mid-30s, a time when many recognize that, perhaps having smoked pot for more than half their lives, it's time for a major reassessment.

Somebody who contacted me recently put it like this:
"I smoke before I go to work, and rush home at the end of the day to get stoned. And there I sit all alone, smoking and watching crap TV. And I thought I was happy. I am wrong in that assessment. By continuing to smoke dope I am wasting my life away, and I no longer wish that for myself. Yet, on the other hand, I am a successful businessperson, own my own place in London, have no significant debts, and have some nice material possessions. Dope has always been there – my comforter, my relaxant, and my friend. Well, that friendship has to end. I want to stop. I want to enjoy my life. I want a relationship. I don't go out, I don't meet people. All I do is sit in and get stoned."

Not everyone who comes to our workshops is in that position. Many are in relationships, have partners, families and active social lives; but what Clearhead clients have in common is that they are tired of being controlled by cannabis. They long for, and are seeking, a life free from the limitations they associate with smoking dope every day.

Another man who came through one of our workshops explained his thoughts about his subtle addiction like this: "As a teenager, smoking was certainly a way of dealing with the problems I faced creating my own reality. In that sense, I think it wasn't a bad thing. It enabled me to become someone else, or at least define myself in a different way. I didn't have to be the square, clever kid but could step away from all that was expected and rebel. The amazing thing is that I've carried on for so long, despite having been in trouble in three countries outside the UK for smoking, despite having a close friend diagnosed with cannabis-induced psychosis back in '82 who's never been the same since, despite being scared deep-down of dying of cancer, as some of my friends have. All of that, and I carried on. I think that was all due to negative self-image … but I don't have that any more. Now I feel I really have accepted that part of the equation, like I've come to my senses at last."

Whilst I accept that everybody has different motivations, part of my own personality has always craved optimum health. Even when my cannabis consumption was at its most outrageous, I longed to know what it felt like to be naturally high. I'd had glimpses from an erratic practice of yoga and meditation, and was able to distinguish between the natural, subtle form of relaxed feelings gained from those activities, and the more chemical, physical dope sensations that would take over after smoking my first post-yoga class joint.

For a long time I fantasized about waking up and feeling *normal* rather than thick-headed and anxious. It wasn't until

I finally found the strength to throw away my cannabis crutch that I slowly began to understand that simply freeing myself from my addiction was a wonderful natural high in itself.

5. Fear and Procrastination

'Productivity is notoriously difficult to predict.'
Alan Greenspan, Chairman of the Board of Governors of the Federal Reserve of the United States (1987-2006)

I have received many benefits since I smoked my last joint. I've grown as a person, I know who I am now, and feel confident in expressing myself. I don't live a secret stoned life anymore, and have had the burden of guilt surrounding my cannabis obsession removed. But perhaps the most practical benefit is that I don't procrastinate like I used to. These days I don't hide away from the tasks I don't want to do. I deal with stuff, and stuff get done.

Many hardcore smokers, no matter how committed, would be honest enough to recognize the syndrome. For me, it was the way I had to have a smoke before I could do … well, almost anything. Go to the shops, make a phone call, leave the house, visit friends, do some work, watch TV, read a book. **Had to have a smoke first.** They say tobacco smokers use cigarettes as punctuation. It's the same with joints of course; but unlike cigarettes, every joint I used to smoke made my mind cloudier, so that I couldn't trust myself to make the right decisions anymore. Things would get put off. Procrastination ruled. This cost me big time:

- Bills wouldn't get paid – I ended up paying surcharges.
- I didn't get it together to communicate properly at work – more expensive mistakes.
- I didn't look for new work opportunities – who knows what I missed out on?
- I didn't call back potential partners after I'd gone out with them – much regret.
- I didn't check my bank statements – I lived in constant fear of bounced payments out of my account.
- I lost good friends who thought I didn't like them, because I never kept in touch – I tended to isolate myself.
- I never got round to starting or finishing projects – life always felt unsatisfying on a deep level.

Psychologists call this *Amotivational Syndrome*, a **characteristic** defined by chronic cannabis abuse, or laziness. I'm not sure about that, as I don't go for this idea that stoners are lazy just because they smoke pot. In my opinion, procrastination is all about fear. Fear of making the wrong decision. Do I really want to be with that person? Do I really need to pay that bill now? Is it worth risking the job that I know for something new? Do I really value myself enough to be worthy of a better lifestyle, of success? Fear is often a major element of cannabis use.

- Paranoid fear.
- Fear of others knowing how much we rely on cannabis.
- Fear of doing or saying the wrong thing when we're stoned.
- Fear of what life might be like without weed.
- Fear of our emotions and our feelings.
- And perhaps most of all, fear of achieving what we are capable of.

Since I've stopped smoking I've found it much easier to trust in myself and trust in life itself. Dope just sort of perpetuated my negative self-image. Stuff didn't get done, and that made me feel bad about myself to the point where the easiest thing to do was have another smoke. The less that got done, the more guilty I would feel. And the more guilty I would feel, well, I'd just smoke some more, creating a vicious circle of inaction.

Cannabis becomes a sort of glue that we tell ourselves we need to stick the different parts of our life together; but just because we *fear* life will be more difficult when we let go of our cannabis prop, it doesn't mean it's true. Often we suspect that life could actually be easier, but our stoned perspective tells us that we have become too dependent, that it's all gone too far, that it's impossible to change.

And so the biggest procrastination event of them all becomes the fact that we fear a future without cannabis, when the reality is just the opposite. What is in fact on offer is a lifestyle free from fear and the consequences of our inaction.

The other aspect of this procrastination is control. When we're smoking heavily, our minds and our lives tend to be confused, so we focus control on the smallest things, conveniently putting off the stuff that really moves our lives forward. We become perfectionists, to the point where tasks become mountains rather than simple everyday responsibilities. When we let go of our dependence on cannabis, life has a way of opening up opportunities to us, or perhaps we are simply more able to recognize them and act upon them when they appear.

This is illustrated by a friend of mine, an artist who was recognized as a talented painter but to whom galleries never offered the career-breaking exhibition she deserved because she never had more than one or two paintings finished at any one time before they were sold. Sometimes she would only produce perhaps three or four paintings a year. She could never bear to finish anything to the point she was satisfied with it. It was a constant frustration to her that she had to take part-time work as a teacher to subsidize her passion. She told herself she could only paint when she was stoned; she wasn't confident around art dealers, or even in her own abilities.

All of this would be typical of many artists, who struggle to sell what they create, but her life was frustrating to her because she wasn't getting the fullest satisfaction from either her creativity or her career. With my encouragement, she decided to experiment with not smoking for a while; and just as she feared, she found herself barely able to start painting with the oil paints that were her usual medium.

After a month of feeling pretty sick about this, she decided to try her hand at watercolours, an altogether different technique, and far quicker. Paintings have to be finished relatively fast or not at all. The process results in the artist having to improvise to a certain extent as the painting evolves, arguably a riskier process than acrylics or oils because there is no going back. Sophie found she had a wonderful talent for watercolour painting. She now travels extensively, painting the different countries that she visits, coming back to London to sell-out exhibitions. She still paints more complex pieces for her own pleasure, but since she has quit cannabis, her life has more balance and has advanced to such a degree it's hardly recognizable.

6. Boredom

'Somebody's boring me ... I think it's me.'

Dylan Thomas, Welsh poet and legend

So many people tell me they smoke dope because they are bored. It was, perhaps inevitably, a Swedish professor who classified four types of boredom.

1. Boredom of situation, such as being trapped on a train without a book.

2. Creative boredom, when we are constantly forced to come up with new things creatively – which can result in writer's block for example.

3. Boredom of satiety, when we have too much of a good thing.

4. Existential boredom, when we have simply become bored with life itself.

Boredom is often considered just part of the human condition, perhaps a by-product of living in a modern society; a rather sad reflection of our values, but real enough in a world where sometimes it feels that we sacrifice our humanity on the altar of entertainment. If we are uncomfortable with boredom, we either have to change ourselves or change our situation; or, of course, we could just go ahead and get stoned or drunk.

One of the things that used to fascinate me about being stoned was how it would allow me to find beauty in extreme ugliness. Ugly buildings, ugly city, a grey day. But now, as someone who hasn't smoked a joint for, at the time of writing, nearly six years, I can report that I haven't lost this perspective. I learnt the lesson that dope taught me – somehow everything in life is alive and has its own vibratory energy. It's like having learnt to ride a bicycle; it can never be unlearnt, it's always with you. I still observe and absorb my external reality in the same way I did when I used to smoke. It's just part of who I am. But now I don't have those feelings of extreme isolation that used to go with it.

There are some people who use pot to help them focus. I have known students who used weed to help them study, or others who have smoked to complete mundane projects at work or at home. Unfortunately, for many smokers sustained attention when stoned is often very difficult. After years of smoking every day without a break, I would find that either my mind would be constantly leaping from one thing to another or it would go into automatic mode and I'd be constantly forgetting things. Or important details would be left out of whatever task I was doing, resulting in continual frustration which eventually became … that's right – extremely boring.

I found reading and learning new things in general caused particular problems. How much easier, therefore, to indulge in relatively passive, unchallenging activities where I could just turn my mind on to remote control and let others take the risks and the glory of real achievement. When stoned, I would spend hours watching crap TV or playing endless computer games. I would go for aimless drives or walks just to steer clear of the 'boring' thing that I was avoiding, such as just simply being present with my partner or my family, or preparing for the next day at work, writing a difficult letter or making an important call.

Ultimately, as a cannabis user, I found life dreary because I rarely allowed myself to experience much that was new or required the full use of my mind. It took many years to realize it, but I became bored with spending so much time being stoned (boredom of satiety). And this was my original motivation for wanting to stop, or at least cut down on my use. My dope smoking had become so habitual that I had forgotten it was possible to live a life without using alcohol or drugs to run away from, or enhance reality.

7. Anxiety, Paranoia and Other Phobias

'There is no such thing as pure pleasure; some anxiety always goes with it.'
Ovid, Roman poet and philosopher

For most confirmed dope smokers an above-average level of anxiety and paranoia comes with the territory. In the first year of running Clearhead workshops, over 60% of attendees told us that they believed cannabis had been responsible for at least one episode of paranoia at some point in the previous few months prior to attending.

As anybody who has suffered a nasty paranoid incident will tell you, it's not a pleasant experience. But individual occurrences, however disagreeable, are not really the worst of it; they are usually relatively short-lived, and the sufferer can generally be 'talked down' to the point where they become calmer and less fearful about whatever was causing the problem. More serious difficulties occur where general levels of anxiety rise to the point where dope smoking begins to significantly affect the everyday mental health of the user, whether from regular panic attacks, an increase in phobic behaviour or, in extreme cases, psychotic episodes.

It's now impossible to refute the evidence that for some genetically pre-disposed individuals, the dangers to their mental health from cannabis are immense. It's a thin line between recreation and recrimination, and governments are right to be concerned about protecting vulnerable individuals from themselves. But this book is about addiction, dependence and denial – which entrap many more people than even the significant minority who suffer extreme cannabis reactions; and Clearhead certainly doesn't have either the moral or medical authority when it comes to questions of prohibition and legislation, on mental health grounds or any other.

I think it's important to consider, however, that the two most active ingredients of cannabis are THC (tetra-hydro-cannabinol) and CBD (cannabidiol). THC is the psycho-active ingredient, which produces the 'stoned' effect; but we also know that it is the ingredient that precipitates psychosis in certain cases, as well as potentially acting as a trigger that can cause a relapse of symptoms among patients who already have a psychotic illness.

CBD, on the other hand, is devoid of the psychological effects associated with THC, but has strong anti-anxiety, and even anti-psychotic effects. In other words, CBD has a calming effect. So it is also easy to see how the drug can trick people suffering from acute paranoia and temporary psychosis into believing that smoking a joint will relieve the symptoms. It won't, because most commercially grown cannabis is cultivated to contain much more THC than CBD. This is surely one of the more obvious paradoxes that exist in cannabis culture.

For the millions of users who smoke every day without exhibiting any of the more extreme mental health symptoms, the problems of anxiety and paranoia can be less severe but also highly debilitating in their own right. Cannabis overuse tends to deliver a kind of continuous low-level anxiety that can affect relationships and situations at home, at work, and on the street.

All drugs have their side-effects. Something as straightforward as aspirin, for example, can cause stomach bleeding in certain circumstances. The side-effect of cannabis is undoubtedly anxiety, which I've observed impacts the ability to trust. Some heavy smokers tend to find it hard to take life at face value, and don't trust others, or situations easily. This naturally has the effect of not allowing them to trust themselves and, in the wider sense, to trust life itself, thus robbing them of their potential to make the most of opportunities that come their way.

One part of our Clearhead workshops I enjoy the most is when the participants begin to realize how much paranoid behaviour they have in common but thought only belonged to them. In every workshop we have people confessing how they would never answer their phone or the door at home. Trusted friends would be given secret codes and knocks. Others around the table laugh in recognition of their own behaviour, relieved to find others held by the same degree of irrational fear.

When I was smoking, I didn't have many episodes of paranoia in which I felt unduly persecuted or threatened by people or situations, but on two occasions I had frightening panic attacks on the London Underground system which left me shaky and embarrassed.

One of my best friends developed a social phobia which made going out and meeting people almost impossible. For years it was far easier for him to stay at home and be stoned all day than find any sort of external life for himself. However, with a lot of encouragement from those that cared about him, finally he was able to go to his doctor about the problem, and was recommended cognitive behavioural therapy (CBT). The treatment gradually gave him the courage to begin to trust in himself again, but the doctor also pointed out that he first had to stop smoking weed for the treatment to be effective.

Another friend of mine had a long-standing phobia relating to her childhood that manifested itself in anxiety about family and friends returning from a journey. Regardless of whether they had been away for a matter of hours or a few weeks, my friend would feel fear in the pit of her stomach around the time of their expected arrival until their safe return. When she quit smoking dope, for an entirely un-connected reason, she lost this phobia and it hasn't returned. On a more basic level, I know of others who have found they miraculously stopped biting their nails or grinding their teeth whilst asleep when they quit smoking dope. For a drug that most people say they use to help them relax, the side-effects can very often be anything but relaxing.

8. Me, Myself, I – Isolation and Depression

'Happiness is not a goal but a by-product of positive action.'
Valerie Grove, British writer and journalist

As my body and mind acclimatized to smoking dope daily, getting high seemed the perfect way to spend as much time as possible. It didn't feel wrong, dangerous or difficult; I just enjoyed life more when my senses were heightened and when I allowed the reality of everyday life to become a little distorted. After a couple of tokes, I seemed to feel the disparate parts of my consciousness clicking into place. It didn't matter any longer that the reality of my life was difficult and full of problems, or that I lived with unresolved painful feelings, or even that the view from my bedroom window looked straight out on to somebody else's bedroom window. All I had to do was smoke a joint and I could shape my external vision pretty much any way that I wanted. As long as I had weed in my pocket, I thought I could survive pretty much anything.

Other drugs were always available, and in my teens and early 20s I tried pretty much everything; however, at some point I came to the conclusion that weed was going to give me pretty much all I needed, and so it became my drug of choice. As my smoking became more of an everyday habit, I stopped taking life so seriously, and I became much less anxious about the future. Feeling good in the here and now was really all that mattered.

What happened to my younger self, the teenager who found such fulfilment in a 10 quid deal?

Well, as the years drifted by my love affair with weed became an obsession. The problem was I didn't get high anymore, I just got stoned – and there is a real difference. I needed to smoke just to feel normal. My tolerance for dope had reached such a point that if the THC in my system fell below a certain level I would feel a deep lack, a terrible emptiness. I had become dependent on weed just to function, albeit on a low energy level. I managed to run a basic programme, to earn enough money to pay the rent and to eat, but it became increasingly difficult to integrate my need to be stoned with other important areas of life.

When running my own business, whether by chance or osmosis, most of the people who came to work for me were also stoners, to one degree or another. (Perhaps it should have been an interview question) Many times we kept the business going by sheer determination. We went through periods where we were so inefficient it seemed we were running a hundred miles an hour just to stand still.

It took many years for me to become involved in an intimate relationship, partly because I was looking for someone whom I could trust not to criticize me for how much I was smoking, but also because I lacked any confidence in my own worthiness to be loved, and I also believed that I was incapable of giving away that private part of myself that I reserved for being stoned. I now see clearly that, to a large extent, my low self-esteem in this area was kept in place by my dope habit.

Too much cannabis definitely reinforces underlying insecurities and anxieties, and a lack of social and sexual confidence had been with me since adolescence. I had always been shy, and dope just gave me an excuse not to bother. I began to isolate myself from all friends and acquaintances, apart from other smokers, who understood and probably shared my unspoken addiction. As I lost the practice of regular social interaction, my confidence lowered still further. I was paranoid and obsessed about how I thought other people judged me. I became lonely and isolated, and without understanding why, I sank into an ongoing depression.

This process took place over many years, and certainly there were periods when things went well for me. I gained some level of respect from others through my work, but I never believed that anything I ever did was good enough. Eventually I found a partner who liked to smoke as much as I did, but we didn't have much of a social life, preferring to stay home in a co-dependent relationship rather than go out and have fun. This sort of scenario, living a cut-down version of life, is of course not confined to habitual dope smokers, but many addictive types seem to have real problems with self-acknowledgement and therefore are prone to depression.

I know high-achievers who have no self-respect, who have found themselves in jobs and relationships for all the wrong reasons because dope enabled them to ignore what was true about themselves and their lives.

I know bright, clever people who have settled for second and third best in their careers because they sacrificed their education, preferring the instant gratification of sparking up another joint rather than getting on with their studies. I have highly creative friends who find it really hard to make positive career decisions because cannabis has robbed them of confidence in themselves and their abilities.

I have lived next to neighbours whose smoking has led them into crippling debt, where the possibility of starting a family became unrealistic until they finally sorted out what was really important to them.

I know attractive men and women who have lost the love of their lives because their ex-partner couldn't live with an addict who wanted just one more joint before going to bed.

These are just some of the depressing life situations which some dope smokers find themselves in, because the drug itself has a way of eating away at our confidence and keeping us stuck.

There is also something else to consider. Our dopamine levels aren't meant to be tuned to such a high pitch on an everyday basis. Maybe a few times a month or the occasional binge, but if you're smoking relentlessly day after day, particularly strong skunk, then is it any wonder you might find it hard to take pleasure in the ordinary things of life? This is when despair can start to take serious hold. Not only can we become trapped in depressing life situations, but we can also forget what it feels like to be simply happy, to appreciate our birthright to take pleasure from simply being alive.

There will always be people who contact Clearhead to tell us that cannabis has never stopped them achieving whatever they wanted in their lives, and I respect that, but there are a significant percentage of users who do find themselves trapped and unfulfilled on a deep level. This is brought about by their dependence on a drug that for many years was a best friend until there came a point where they found themselves unable to free themselves from its spell.

9. Cannabis and Relaxation

'Relaxing means releasing all concern and tension and letting the natural order of life flow through one's being.'

Donald Curtis, new thought speaker and writer

Scratch the surface of any dope smoker and they will tell you that they smoke to relax; scratch a little deeper and quite a few will tell you that they can't relax without it. This can be a problem, because if you are using cannabis as your primary, or your only, means of relaxation, you have probably forgotten how to relax naturally. Of course, relaxation can mean different things; it's relative. If I finish doing one thing that is particularly stressful, when I stop I relax; I might even smoke a joint.

If I believe my life as a whole to be stressful, then I might rationalize that smoking weed every day is simply the best way of coping, to the point where the best way becomes the only way, regardless of any negative side-effects.

But simply coping with life by spending large parts of it stoned is never going to be a totally relaxed solution. Many people find it much easier to let weed pacify them, rather than deal with the root of what makes their lives disappointing, painful or unsatisfying; in other words, the things cause stress in the first place.

Of course, it's not just potheads. Plenty of us find it easier to stay trapped in a job we hate, a destructive situation or a painful relationship. But very often dope will make things bearable. Whilst this is okay in the short term, when we are smoking hard, the days and months have a way of creeping into years. Progress can therefore be painfully slow, and we often live with a real fear of instigating the sort of necessary confrontation, which can start us on the road to bettering our circumstances.

Change requires risk, and risk entails effort. **Change, risk** and **effort** – three words that some dedicated dope smokers are rather uncomfortable with. Better to stick with what we know, even if it keeps us trapped and makes us unhappy.

Quite a few people who attend our workshops *do* make other significant changes in the months that follow. William applied for a job opportunity in Sydney, Australia; Kerry handed in her notice from a particularly stressful job; and Dan started relationship counselling with his partner. But usually, for most people, it's enough just to get used to not smoking dope every day, without the extra pressure of making immediate, dramatic, life-changing decisions. Often when we quit smoking dope we find we are able to re-engage with our jobs or relationships with a fresh level of commitment, as we see more clearly the possibilities that open up to us. We spend less time *relaxing* and more time actually busy with the process of living.

Like any sticking-plaster solution, using cannabis to relax can become overdone to the point where it ceases to be fully effective any longer. It simply becomes a habit that we find impossible to break. This may sound harsh, but I think much of the time we kid ourselves that we smoke to relax, when it would be more accurate to say that we smoke to anaesthetize ourselves. When pressed on this point, Ken, one of the guys in a Clearhead workshop, admitted that, when it came down to it, relaxation wasn't the issue, he was smoking to manage his anger.

There are perhaps more positive ways to channel our anger than using a substance to pacify ourselves. Personally I used to find that, after a while, smoking dope didn't work like it used to any more. My anger would seep out as irritability and frustration.

Today's hydroponically grown skunk is strong stuff, even if you are used to smoking it and have built up tolerance. Smoking skunk day after day, or night after night, will induce all sorts of conscious and unconscious behaviours, but I would hesitate to say that relaxation is one of them. For me, these days being relaxed has an element of alertness, which has more to do with being calm and clear in my thinking rather than feeling anxious and disengaged from everything around me, which was ultimately the effect that long-term skunk smoking had on my mind.

Another of the problems with using weed to relax occurs when we have to do something we don't want to do and we're stoned at the time. This can happen with even simple things like surprise phone calls, unexpected visitors, or being called on to perform a job that requires some quick thinking. That's when being stoned can be anything but relaxing. We can't focus, we have to think hard when performing even simple tasks, and this can lead to feelings of anxiety and paranoia. Not a very relaxing experience.

I used to smoke dope through the evening while also drinking copious cups of coffee just to try and keep awake, because my energy levels were always so unpredictable. Dope wasn't relaxing me. Along with the coffee, I used it to keep me wired. Like many other dedicated potheads, I would usually stay up until the early hours, doing not very much apart from just not going to bed. I used to rationalize this as 'me time' – just me and Mr Weed relaxing watching late night TV, playing computer games, listening to music on my headphones, or occasionally finishing off a work project that could have been finished weeks ago.

All of this was fine when I was younger, but as my teens gave way to my 20s, and my 20s gave way to my 30s and ultimately my 40s, I existed on not enough sleep. This eventually resulted in burnout. My lifestyle was unhealthy and ultimately unsustainable. Although I did my best to keep going, my batteries were so run down that when I finally learnt to relax naturally the relief was indescribable.

Today I'm more in control of my energy. I can sense when I haven't had enough sleep, and if possible I will prioritize an early night, without feeling I'm missing out on anything. I love the feeling of waking up next morning actually feeling refreshed rather than washed out and groggy from the dope session the night before.

If I need to relax, I relax naturally with a simple bath or a shower, or perhaps I'll just lie on the floor with my eyes shut, practising some of the breathing techniques I learnt from yoga classes. Maybe I'll call someone who I know will cheer me up and who would appreciate hearing from me. Or I might rent a particular movie or watch a specific television programme that I can now enjoy without feeling guilty like I used to when I would indiscriminately watch endless hours of TV.

If I'm feeling restless, overwhelmed or emotional, I try and do something physical to channel my feelings through my body. My solution is usually a vigorous bike ride; others might swim, go to the gym, or take a regular class in martial arts, Pilates, dance or tai chi. Wherever you live there is usually some possibility for physical exercise, even if it's just taking somebody else's dog for a walk. Relaxation doesn't have to be as mind numbing as I thought it needed to be when I was caught up in a cycle of stress, weed and zoned-out inertia.

10. Self-medication and Medical Marijuana

'The trouble with always trying to preserve the health of the body is that it is so difficult to do without destroying the health of the mind.'
G.K. Chesterton, English novelist and poet

Whether we literally *like* it or not, in most countries cannabis is part of the fabric of life, if only on the basis of how widely it is consumed. Unfortunately, the political controversy surrounding the issue has limited under-standing about context of use. This lack of awareness applies to many users, as well as those who legislate on the issue.

For every pothead who is simply toking to enjoy the sensation, there are others who use cannabis in an attempt to self-medicate in some way – whether to gain relief from pain brought about by physical sickness, or perhaps from injury, insomnia, emotional trauma, depression, or even some degree of mental illness.

'Medical marijuana' is *the* frontline issue for legalizers and prohibitionists alike, especially in America, where some state laws allow 'cannabis dispensaries' to offer patients weed by licence for a variety of different medical conditions, whilst cultivation, supply and consumption are still banned by federal law.

The arguments on both sides are passionate and un-compromising, similar to how Americans are divided by abortion and capital punishment.

Pro-legalizers find it difficult to appreciate that medical marijuana is always likely to be abused as a potentially addictive and dangerous substance, whilst many prohib-itionists will not compromise on a position that dismisses medicinal cannabis as nothing more than a foot in the door to the legalization of all prohibited drugs.

Most medical experts clearly believe that with such a wide choice of prescribed solutions available there is no need for medicinal cannabis, whilst to counter that argument hard-core liberalizers offer conspiracy theories concerning vested interests between Government and the pharmaceutical industry as the only thing keeping marijuana illegal in the United States.

It's interesting to consider how cannabis might work as a pain reliever. I once got into a conversation with someone who smoked dope to help deal with chronic pain that developed from an industrial injury to his leg. He explained that it wasn't so much that getting stoned stopped the pain itself, but rather that his mind tended not to fixate on the pain in the same way as when he hadn't been smoking.

For a long time, smoking cannabis as a method of delivery was cited as an obvious reason why medical marijuana would always be considered unworkable. But today, the recommended methods of delivery, are either orally or by a vaporizer contraption thought to be the safest way of inhaling marijuana. It works by using a heating element to cook the drug to just below the point of combustion so that a vapour is produced rather than smoke, bypassing the carcinogens and other toxins associated with smoking weed through a joint or a pipe.

Personally I find it difficult not to be moved by stories of terminally sick people who are denied the right to choose their own medication without harassment.

On a different tack when I began to question my own relationship with cannabis, it amazed me that I chose a drug almost guaranteed in the long-term to make my mild dyslexic/dispraxic symptoms even more pronounced. Being stoned as an adult badly affected my balance, my rhythm, my hand-to-eye coordination and my sense of direction, but something about cannabis seemed to help my condition in the early days of my using and as I began to work with others, I saw that I was by no means the only one who had learning differences at school and who chose to smoke dope as a way of coping. I'm also aware there are some high-achieving students who smoke to relieve the pressure of expectation from teachers and family.

In some countries there is a small but vocal number of young people who believe that self-medicating with cannabis offers a more effective, and more natural treatment for attention deficit disorder and attention deficit/hyper-activity disorder than the heavily prescribed Ritalin.

Understandably, almost all medical specialists of these conditions would argue that cannabis only aggravates the symptoms, or even causes them in the first place, but perhaps it might be possible to consider that beyond issues of legality certain young people are better suited to one type of drug than another to moderate their behaviour. Not necessarily herbal cannabis, but possibly a synthesized version might be an option.

Numerous people tell me that they smoke dope to help alleviate their depression. The fact that so many smokers use cannabis as a sleep aid is a clue to this connection. Sleep and mood are intimately related, and sleep disturbance is an integral part of depressive illness. There are a range of depressive disorders, from deep clinical depression to relatively short episodes, and in the long term, cannabis use is unlikely to be helpful for those suffering at either end of the spectrum.

The problem is that the use of **any** drug – whether bought off the street or prescribed by your doctor – over an extended period to treat every aspect of depression may be counter-productive. Surely chemical interventions should ideally only be temporary solutions. Taking any sort of drug for depression long term can stop us from balancing ourselves physically and emotionally, when we could be working through and healing the underlying problems through talking and physical therapies. Many cannabis users smoke in addition to taking anti-depressants, which in itself can only reduce the effectiveness of their prescription.

As discussed earlier; at the milder end of the depressive spectrum smoking dope very often keeps us stuck in life situations that are the root cause of our depression in the first place, and can keep sufferers uninterested in improving their general health through exercise and nutrition, which are acknowledged as two key routes to holistic depression management.

It is undeniable that millions of people use hard drugs, alcohol and, of course, cannabis to screen themselves from deep emotional trauma. Childhood trauma affects different people in different ways. It doesn't have to involve abuse; there are degrees of emotional pain. Parental absence, lack of love, and peer bullying will have profoundly diverse effects on different youngsters, depending on other variables. Bearing this in mind, if you are smoking dope as a medicine for emotional pain, you may well be correct in considering it to be a relatively safe option. I accept this, but I also appreciate the power of stretching ourselves beyond what we sometimes think is possible to achieve.

Life is short, and getting shorter every day, and although many of us go through periods of profound depression brought about by the circumstances we find ourselves in, does this mean we have to give up on the possibility of one day experiencing positive feelings such as self acceptance, joy, and gratitude, which are often so hard to achieve when we are self-medicating? Yes, we can fleetingly experience these emotions through alcohol, cannabis, or cocaine, but so often we pay in hard currency once their effects wear off or they cease to be effective over the long term.

11. Cannabis and Alcohol

The following passage is based on a newspaper article discussing middle-class drinking habits.

My name is Jane I accept that I'm a relatively heavy drinker. My friends are always telling me that I should cut down my consumption, but in my opinion I don't drink any more than they do, although I certainly drink every day. During the week I will start after work, either at the pub with my work colleagues or, more commonly, as soon as I get home. When I come through the door, usually the first thing I do is pour myself a drink. If I'm by myself, during the week my average consumption would be about half a bottle of wine each evening, usually drunk while sitting and watching TV.

On the weekend I usually start with some light drinking from around midday. If I'm out for a meal in the evening with my boyfriend or a group of friends, I often end up finishing a bottle of wine by myself, sometimes together with cocktails. If I'm at a party I'll probably drink two bottles of wine, maybe more.

Depending on what is going on in my life, my average alcohol consumption would be between five and ten bottles of wine a week, or around 70 units of alcohol. I am aware that the government-recommended limit is 20.

I can barely remember a time when I haven't woken up with a hangover, but it usually clears within an hour or so, and I never let how I feel the morning after dissuade me from drinking later in the day. I just enjoy the experience of drinking too much to let it. I certainly don't consider myself an alcoholic. If I really wanted to I could go without alcohol, and once a year I sometimes do try and have a couple of weeks without drinking, to clear out my system, though I admit I find it really hard. For me, a life without a few drinks is a life not worth living.

You wouldn't need to change too much from Jane's testimony to imagine that it was written by any experienced dope smoker talking honestly about his or her pattern of use. Heavy cannabis smoking like heavy drinking is a lifestyle choice each with its own particular pleasures and risks.

Most dope smokers have a complex relationship with alcohol, even if they don't drink. When I was 17 I was sick with a liver disease, meaning that for a year – and a prime drinking year for a young adult at that – my liver was unable to process alcohol. It was during that year that my love affair with cannabis was consummated. As a confirmed stoner, I developed very little interest in alcohol or what could be loosely termed 'alcohol culture'. I'm not alone. There are plenty of other dope smokers who don't enjoy alcohol or boozy situations, and some look upon the average drinker with a feeling of moral superiority.

There is a deep resentment at the heart of cannabis culture that alcohol is the world's acceptable drug. Most experienced dope smokers believe without question that alcohol is the more dangerous of the two, not only for the individual but also for society as a whole, and the medical and social welfare statistics bear this out. Of course quite understandably, people who have seen the negative consequences will point to the potential and highly specific dangers to mental health from smoking even small amounts of cannabis.

Interestingly, within the traditions of alcohol culture there is a counter-sense of not trusting those that don't drink. Confirmed old boozers such as Winston Churchill and W.C. Fields sincerely believed that abstinence was a sign of weakness of character. Ties of friendship and loyalty are still bound tight by drinking as a ritual for social bonding.

These days, for more and more of us, the two drug cultures overlap and are interlocked to such an extent that individually and collectively, they are not only capable of offering real pleasure, but, unfortunately, also hold the potential for genuine distress. If you're a pot smoker reading that last sentence with a degree of cynicism, take note of this random email posted on the Clearhead message boards:

After reading other messages this one is going to sound pretty much the same story. Smoking for twenty years, trying to stop for at least the last ten, failed on numerous occasions and cannot imagine being clean of this drug which I have grown to despise. My son, my health indeed my life and the quality of it does not stop me from smoking this crap every day. I spend every waking hour thinking about stopping and this leads to more smoking to alleviate the stress!!!!! I have depression and serious asthmatic problems both of which obviously are not helped by smoking, but the biggest crime of all that I commit alongside cannabis is wasting time alone that I should be spending with my beautiful boy.

Alcohol and cannabis are the world's most widely used mood-altering drugs, and clearly people can run into trouble using either.

It is widely believed that approximately 10% of people who smoke cannabis become dependent on the drug to some extent, but a pot smoker who smokes throughout the day is likely to be more functional than someone who is drinking to the same extent. The downside of this discrepancy is that dependency and addiction creep up on you in a more subtle fashion if you smoke dope than if you have alcoholic tendencies.

At Marijuana Anonymous meetings I met quite a few recovering alcoholics who upon first discovering weed thought they had found the perfect way to avoid the dangerous situations they would get themselves into when drunk. However, because they couldn't drink with moderation, they also found it impossible to use cannabis with any self-control, often allowing isolation to replace the reckless confidence that was the hallmark of their drinking. On another level, some realized that they were swapping potential liver disease for the risk of severe respiratory problems if they carried on smoking the tobacco joints they were addicted to.

Maybe it would be useful at this stage to remind ourselves why we drink alcohol, take cocaine or smoke pot. Of course, from the dawn of time mankind has always sought to change consciousness, or perhaps even lose consciousness, and from an early age adolescent drinkers quickly discover that alcohol makes socializing an awful lot easier. Many young adults lack confidence, and drinking is a convenient, socially acceptable shortcut to letting go of social and sexual inhibitions. Additionally, alcohol has always been used as a relaxant to relieve us from life's stresses and strains, and as an anaesthetic when our emotional lives become too intense.

People use cocaine and other party drugs, such as ecstasy or speed, in a similar way. Some people like to use coke whilst they are drinking so that they can keep going for longer; or whilst working, to give them extra confidence and energy. Cannabis, on the other hand, is generally used as a stress reliever first and a social drug second. For most people, working while stoned is not a brilliant career move, but many do so just the same because they are bored. Mature cannabis smokers tend to prefer smoking alone or in a quiet group rather than in a raucous party atmosphere. It's no accident that the larger cannabis cafés in Amsterdam are securely separated from the loud bars and pubs that share the same premises.

For many, chain smoking weed at the end of a night's cocaine and alcohol fueled partying is the only thing that allows wind down and some sleep.

It's fair to say that people's problems with alcohol and cannabis dependency can range through mild, moderate and severe; and there are some important variables to consider. For example, binge drinking has become an increasingly common phenomenon. This might mean drinking to excess on occasion, but not every day. In the UK there are government-recommended guidelines as to how many units of alcohol per week it is safe to consume. Some definitions classify binge drinking as when half the week's alcohol units are consumed in one session. A hard-core dope smoker, on the other hand, might smoke all day, every day, from morning till night, as I did. Others smoke during all their free time, which could mean every minute of the day when not working. Evidently, it is possible to function at a reasonable level as a heavy smoker or as a heavy drinker without necessarily being classed as an addict, but there will come a breaking point. There always does. Our minds and bodies are designed for optimum health, not long-term abuse.

I used to think alcohol was a more extreme drug than cannabis, both in terms of its physical and behavioural effects, but today's skunk has made me re-think this. And there are no guidelines, government-recommended or otherwise, as to how many weekly THC skunk units are safe for consumption.

Many people just love that out of control feeling they get from a long cannabis and alcohol session. Bluntly, this can be a dangerous combination, if only because the closer you are to blacking out at the edge of oblivion, the more vulnerable you are to both accidents and others seeking to take advantage of your condition.

Nothing about drinking or drugging is particularly safe or healthy, and as a society we continue to argue about the rights of personal freedom and responsibility. Perhaps it would be more constructive to remind ourselves at what age we start experimenting with mood-altering drugs. Here in the UK, 2005 statistics show that 45% of 14- to 15-year-olds have an average alcohol consumption of 10.4 units a week; and 10% of 11- to 12-year-old boys binge drink more than 5 units in a single session. There is no gender gap; 15-year-old girls are drinking more than boys. In the same period, 12% of all school children used cannabis, including 33% of all 15-year-olds. (Source: *Addicted Britain*, study by the Centre for Social Justice.)

Clearly, lots of us can drink or smoke dope appropriately, but the younger we start, the harder it is to exercise control when we run into problems in later life; and those problems can be triggered by any number of painful circumstances that can affect us during the course of a lifetime.

Drug prohibition and responsible drinking advertising doesn't seem to have changed the negative health and social impact of alcohol and drug abuse. The issue will always be one of **effective** education. As a progressive society, it would be really useful to teach our children healthier ways to gain confidence other than getting drunk, and more natural paths to relaxation and healthy sleep rather than smoking dope. It would also make sense to teach children from a very early age, how to understand and recognize when they are feeling angry, tired, scared or sad, and how to learn to process these feelings safely and appropriately.

12. Cannabis and Tobacco

'Stupid risks make life worth living.'
H. Simpson, American television actor and family man

It's no surprise I became fascinated, then obsessed, and ultimately addicted to cannabis. I was certainly interested in the whole process of smoking from a very early age. My Mum, whilst she was alive, was a heavy cigarette smoker, so ashtrays, lighters and cigarette packets followed her wherever she went. She even used to keep a strange little portable ashtray with a lid on it in her handbag, just in case she ever found herself in a situation where she needed a discreet nicotine hit.

Toward the end of her life, just as smokers began to be demonized, Mum became a lot less discreet and much more militant about her habit. She stopped caring completely about what anybody thought. In the days when you could just about get away with it, she would smoke in restaurants, hospitals, school playgrounds, doctors' waiting rooms – anywhere, really. From the age of around 10 I started to experiment on my own, stealing the odd cigarette from her. By the time I was 17, Mum accepted I was going to be a cigarette smoker, and it was okay to smoke in front of her. From then on we used to smoke together, often sharing cigarettes, and she was genuinely disappointed in me when I made my first attempt at quitting tobacco on my 30th birthday. I could never tell her that I smoked cannabis, of course. She had a hatred of drugs.

My Dad had a different attitude to cigarettes; he never touched them except every New Year's Eve, when Mum used to make him smoke one for a laugh. My Dad knew that tobacco was bad news healthwise, so he offered us kids a financial inducement to remain non-smokers up until our 18th birthdays. My sisters got their reward, but I never made it.

I remember at age 12, the week before starting at a new school, Dad giving me a long, serious talk about the risks of smoking. He talked about cancer and heart attacks, and used my favourite footballers as role models; but even though I was hearing what he was saying, I wasn't listening. The first day at school, at the earliest opportunity, I was behind the bike sheds with the rest of the guys. How glad I was to have taught myself to smoke properly so I wasn't embarrassed in front of my new friends. As you can see, I was getting mixed messages from both parents. At 13 I definitely knew the risks. Smoking was bad for you, but so what? It was also fun, a bit naughty, and pretty cool.

According to the stepping-stone theory of addiction, we increase risk relative to surviving risk. So when as a young teen smoker I figured out that there wasn't an immediate deterioration to my health, it was easy enough to think that the warnings about drugs, especially dope, given out by adults were exaggerated as well. But we all have different stories. I know plenty of people who have hardly ever smoked a cigarette in their lives but are addicted to nicotine just the same because of smoking tobacco joints from an early age.

Smoking tobacco joints is a huge problem here in the UK, as in many other countries. The cocktail of the two drugs is deadly; not only because of the way we smoke it, holding the smoke deep in our lungs to extract the maximum value from every unfiltered toke, but also the way that, for a tobacco joint smoker, the cravings for nicotine and cannabis become confused and make nicotine addiction a much harder habit to break than for the average cigarette smoker who has never smoked dope.

As ever with cannabis, there are conflicting health reports. Recent studies at the Harvard Cancer Center in Boston have revealed that human lung cancer tumours grew less than half as fast in mice that were injected with moderate doses of THC. This isn't exactly great news for American parents trying to warn their children about the dangers of marijuana, and dope smokers generally need zero excuses to defend their hobby. It seems unlikely, however, that health professionals are going to start encouraging us all to use cannabis to protect ourselves from lung cancer.

At the other end of the scare spectrum, there are continuing studies showing that smoking cannabis and tobacco together, not even necessarily in the same cigarette, increases the risk of contracting **chronic obstructive pulmonary disease** (surely as nasty as it sounds) by a third more than smoking tobacco alone. Emphysema is another concern. The respiratory department at St Mary's Hospital in London is finding more and more people are contracting this disease in their 30s, presenting lungs that look like they belong to a 65- year-old. The common link? Tobacco joints.

For a long time in Britain and most of Europe it was easier to buy hashish than herbal cannabis. It's impossible to roll a hashish joint without another substance to help it burn, and so the tobacco joint became the most popular way to smoke dope. Since about the year 2000, however, the availability of herbal cannabis has increased to the point where most people prefer to smoke weed than hash. So, in theory, you would expect more people to now smoke their herbal cannabis without tobacco. But tradition, like addiction, is hard to break, and the fact is that almost all British dope smokers are heavily addicted to the cocktail of the two drugs. At the present time, because of legal issues, I can't really see the likelihood of a government campaign advising cannabis users to smoke dope without tobacco. However the truth is that significant numbers of school-age children have bypassed cigarettes, and are simply addicted to tobacco joints. We really need to cut through the hypocrisy and get a high profile information campaign out on this point right now, but for the authorities the political implications would possibly be a step too far.

The good news from a health perspective is that, at the time of writing, Europe has created powerful legislation which will mark the beginning of the end for cigarettes as the addiction of the masses. New generations of young women will find other ways to suppress their appetites; young men will find other ways to be cool; and cigarettes will be thrown into the dustbin of history within 30 years. In July 2008, Amsterdam's cafés will have to be non-smoking and follow the same rules as other, more ordinary public places. Eventually 'viral cool' rather than any Government information campaign will ensure that most of the new generation of Europe's dope smokers will smoke weed without tobacco.

But for now we have a massive problem helping people who might want to quit weed, quit tobacco, or try and quit both together. Perhaps we need to start by honestly accepting that cannabis, alcohol and tobacco are the recreational drugs of choice for millions of people. Maybe they shouldn't, but today, more than ever, people drink too much alcohol, smoke too much dope, and are addicted to nicotine.

Cannabis, alcohol and tobacco go together really well. You're in the pub having a few drinks and the alcohol triggers your urge for nicotine. Loads of people fall off the nicotine wagon because they can't seem to enjoy a beer or a glass of wine without a cigarette. For the dope smoker who likes a drink as well, the urge is even more frustrating, because what they really want is a tobacco joint to go with whatever they are drinking. The cigarette ban in pubs and clubs perversely seems to have changed the order of things. Previously many dope smokers aware that they couldn't light a joint in public would avoid these sorts of places because they didn't smoke cigarettes. Today with smokers of all description corralled into smoking outside the premises, a discreet cannabis joint is almost unnoticeable in the general fug.

Drug harm reduction experts would urge you to go home and smoke your weed in a vaporizer; but if you are addicted to cannabis joints, that's really not going to do the trick. So where do you start? Many people come to us at Clearhead not because of mental health problems, not because of what cannabis is doing to their heads, not even because of addiction, but simply because they don't want to die young from smoking such a deadly cocktail. And this is where it gets serious.

You have to take responsibility for your own health

If you feel that tobacco is slowly killing you, you have to take steps to quit. There is plenty of support out there for you.

If you feel that you are drinking too much, you have to come to an honest decision as to whether you are an alcoholic or simply a heavy drinker. Have you lost control of your drinking? If so, then if you value what you still have in your life, perhaps you should finally admit the problem and seek help.

If you feel that smoking dope makes you, confused, anxious and stupefied, and that it is keeping you stuck in situations that you are fed up with, I would suggest it's time to quit smoking weed.

In that case...
Could you be an ex-dope smoker who now has the occasional drink to get a buzz on?

Or…

Could you be an ex-tobacco joint smoker who still smokes weed (without tobacco), but now with control?

Or…

Could you be an ex-alcoholic or hard drug user who feels lucky every day that you are now only addicted to nicotine?

These are decisions you have to make for yourself to find out what you want from the rest of your life; and there is usually a process of trial and error to see what you are capable of in your present circumstances. Some people for example quit tobacco but still smoke dope on its own, often quite heavily for a while, until they finally decide they can't handle it. The next section of this book will help you examine that possibility.

Others are ready to quit weed and would love to not smoke cigarettes – but one thing at a time. The last two sections of the book will help you understand how this process works.

13. Cannabis and Couples

'There were three of us in this marriage.'
Diana, Princess of Wales

The young man raised his head, looking close to tears, and in a quiet voice said, "My name is Vince and I'm a marijuana addict." In the few weeks I had been coming to Marijuana Anonymous meetings I'd heard similar declarations, but there was an emotional intensity to Vince that I hadn't witnessed with the others. He was shaking and seemed in a really bad way. As he told us his story I began to understand why. His wife had been six-months pregnant when he lost his job; Vince admitted that the reasons for his dismissal came down to his cannabis habit, which had made him unreliable and inefficient. He told the meeting that although his wife was aware he was smoking a lot, she didn't understand how negatively his daily intake was affecting him.

For the next few months, until the birth of his daughter, he had made attempts to find a new job but had come up with nothing. Because of the way his last job had ended, he found it difficult to even get interviews for anything close to his previous position. His confidence, never great, had dwindled to the point where he had given up even applying. The only thing that felt safe to him was staying at home with the curtains drawn, smoking weed and not answering the phone. Meanwhile, his wife worked for as long as she could before the birth. In those last few weeks whilst she remained at home, Vince would leave the house pretending to be doing temporary work for a friend, but got no further than either the local park or shopping centre, where he would spend his days stoned, anxious and depressed.

He promised himself that when his baby was born he would finally get it together to quit smoking weed and get his life back on track. He came clean to his wife about the reality of his cannabis habit and how it was affecting him. They agreed that, after the birth, he would take any job he could find. The problem was that, even after their son was born, Vince couldn't quit smoking for more than a few days, maybe a week or so, and now he had to hide from his wife when stoned, which meant he wasn't coming home as promptly as he should. Although by now Vince was working, he was earning less money than was needed. All of this put huge pressure on the relationship, until trust was broken to the point where his wife asked him to leave.

That was two days before I first met Vince. He was now living with his mum, and here he was, at his first MA meeting, full of regret and self-loathing. I gave him my telephone number at the meeting, and over the next few months got to know him well. We supported each other, and I began to see that both our issues with cannabis had to do with commitment phobia – mine with fear of making a positive commitment to myself, and his with the fact that he didn't feel he could live up to his marriage commitments. Slowly, over a time of abstinence, we began to see that smoking weed had, to a large extent, been responsible for keeping our anxiety and fears in place, as well as damaging our self-confidence. The longer we went without smoking, and with the help of regular counselling, the easier it became to keep our relationships and responsibilities in perspective, and understand more about what it was that was causing the fear in the first place.

Claire emailed me at Clearhead about a month before she was due to attend a workshop. Her partner had researched us on the Internet and suggested she come along. When she introduced herself to the others in the group, she could barely speak because she was so angry. When people come along to a Clearhead weekend, they know that they will be given the option of one final smoking session on the Saturday night and that it's going to be their last one, for a while or possibly forever. Some people will smoke heavily right up to the end, others will taper down or even quit a few days before as their supply runs out. Needless to say, it's a very personal decision.

In Claire's case, her boyfriend had taken that decision for her by throwing away what was left of her grass, three days before the weekend. She was furious, upset, and felt tricked into coming. Someone asked her why she didn't simply go and buy some more and tell her boyfriend to go to hell. It turned out that Claire relied on her boyfriend to score for her. He had been doing so for a long time, on the grounds that he didn't want her *associating with undesirables*, and she didn't know where to go and buy dope for herself. Clearly, although perhaps unconsciously, he was controlling her; first by buying her weed, and then by telling her he thought it would be a good idea if she quit. It might have been a good idea for him, but it certainly wasn't, at that precise moment, right for Claire, who, although ready to explore the possibilities of abstinence, hadn't been allowed to make her own decision and mentally prepare herself properly.

A week or so later, Claire's partner called me on our helpline. He was concerned, but also angry, because he thought we should know that apparently Claire had persuaded one of the other participants in her group to score some weed for her. Claire's relationship with her partner was a classic case of co-dependency which had got out of hand. An aspect of co-dependency is where one person is either controlling another person or allowing themselves to be controlled, usually because there is something fundamental lacking in their own life.

Claire clearly wasn't ready to stop smoking. As long as quitting was part of her boyfriend's control mechanism and she was doing it for him rather than herself, it was never going to work. Not until she truly believed she was ready to change and was motivated, would she be ready to quit.

One way or another, relationship issues are a frequent trigger leading people to address their cannabis smoking. When I was answering calls to the MA helpline, we had a constant stream of men and women calling in desperation, just wishing that those close to them had been able to make the call themselves. So many told me that their partners had changed for the worse as their smoking had accelerated, and yet somehow they couldn't seem to see that cannabis was causing any problems. The trouble is that when we become addicted to any substance or behaviour it can often become more important than those closest to us. Cannabis addicts can become isolated, secretive and unreliable, somehow never fully present to even those we care most deeply about. Of course we aren't. Our minds are almost always literally somewhere else.

Naturally, couples often smoke together, and this can make the dynamics of shared use really hard to unravel. Perhaps one partner might smoke recreationally for enjoyment, whilst for the other it is really a problem for them to have cannabis in the home because they need to smoke addictively every single day.

Freya contacted me about three months before one of our workshops, wanting some advice. She felt she was ready to quit cannabis but didn't want to lose the relationship with her long-term partner Jamie, who she said had no intention of quitting. She was worried that it was their shared love of smoking dope that kept them together, as much as their love for each other. I told her that quitting can be quite literally a life-changing step and that once the green-tinted spectacles were removed, the relationship was bound to change – maybe for the better, maybe for the worse. But in the first instance, I explained, she had to quit for herself, even if it was simply to discover who she really was without being stoned all of the time. If Freya really wanted to see what life could be like without dope, we would give her every support; and if she was able to quit, I felt sure she would gain some real perspective about her life, and of course her relationship.

Two weeks before the workshop, a big surprise. Freya emailed again, this time asking whether there was space for Jamie on the weekend as well as her, because he had *seen the light*. That was when I got worried. I figured that Jamie must have been feeling threatened by the situation and was only prepared to come along so that he could pick holes in our work and undermine Freya's commitment to change. When Jamie sent back his form giving us the reasons he wanted to quit, they actually seemed entirely reasonable – lack of energy and motivation at work, irritability, bad sleep, and a fear of losing Freya. I agreed to let them attend together but feared the worst.

Meeting Freya and Jamie at the workshop made me consider things differently. Freya, like most people who attend our weekend, was fearful about quitting, but in her case to the point of terror. She was very emotional. It emerged that her smoking had increased dramatically over the last 12 months, since her sister was diagnosed with a serious illness. She wanted to stop, however, because she saw that dope was isolating her to the point where she and Jamie barely had a social life. She was also definitely using weed as a way of not working through the fear she held about her sister's health.

Jamie, on the other hand, was resolute that he was ready to quit; he was mentally prepared and had started to cut down. He had also decided to take control of his life by looking for a new job, because his existing work was causing him too much stress. Over the course of the weekend I began to see that Jamie was going to find the whole process much easier than Freya, which taught me about the value of being really honest with ourselves as to why we smoke and how best to prepare for change.

Mia attended another workshop. She was a smart lady in her mid-40s who shared her life with her husband Chris, who had quit cannabis himself a long time ago. At the end of the weekend Mia addressed the group in a strong, positive voice, telling us that something had clicked for her and, as much as she had loved weed and in the past had spent many wonderful times getting high, she felt ready to move on and reclaim her life, which had become muddled and foggy. Seldom had I seen someone more collected or more determined at this stage.

Mia called me each week over the following months. "Stopping smoking wasn't the problem," she told me, "it's my family." Every day that passed without smoking, it became obvious to Mia that her being muddled and foggy suited Chris just fine. He had been getting away with a lot for years, gambling and spending the money they had earned together. Chris much preferred Mia stoned, as did one or two other family members, who also had taken advantage of Mia emotionally for a long time. Mia was angry, to the point of seeking separation.

It's really not a good idea to make significant life changes in the first twelve months of recovery from addiction. Suddenly changing a job or starting a relationship are decisions that might be regretted shortly after, so I was really concerned about the idea of a separation. I asked Mia to persuade Chris to come with her for couple counselling, and happily enough it worked. With the help of a skilled family therapist they both trusted, they talked through their very real problems to get back in touch with the reasons why they had fallen in love with each other 20 years previously.

When I was smoking dope, I knew a lovely couple whose life together revolved around weed – talking about it, scoring it, and of course smoking it. At different points of the year, like clockwork, one of them would decide it was time to quit, but unfortunately never together at the same time. The problem for them, as it is for many other couples in a similar situation, was one of timing. If you are both genuinely ready at the same time, it does make the process easier.

It's perfectly possible, however, for a couple to quit separately, but the person still smoking has to be totally supportive and unthreatened by their partner's decision. Practically speaking, that means – not smoking in the same room, preferably not even smoking in the home. Go out to the garden, or go for a discreet walk round the block, and take the dog with you if you have one. Just don't be blowing smoke in your partner's direction, and show lots of love and understanding.

If you are still smoking and your partner is going through the process of quitting, encourage them. You will almost certainly have to put up with their emotional outbursts for the first few weeks or so. Learn to be positive in the face of their mood swings and their irrational temper tantrums. It will be intense while it lasts, but it won't last forever. Even if they have a minor relapse, keep encouraging them; don't immediately use it as an excuse to get back to your old habits of smoking together. Give the process a chance. In other words, let the love you feel for your partner transcend your own love of weed.

My co-founder of Clearhead, Adrienne, quit about six months before her husband. Both her son and her husband were still smoking, but not in the house. Adrienne was determined to stop, if only to show her son that she could, and to encourage him to quit himself. Adrienne was fairly dramatic about her decision. She told everybody she knew and changed quite a few things in her life. She started going to the gym, improved her diet, took up hobbies and changed her daily routines.

Six months later her husband just quietly quit one day, after having smoked for 35 years, and never started again. He never even told her, and Adrienne didn't realize for a week or so. Her son also quit that year; first by not smoking in front of her, then not in the house, until finally he saw how weed was isolating him and doing little for his future prospects. He had learnt from his mum that it was possible to quit.

Quitting together

Team effort, support each other, **expect a row**, remember your motivation, **accept your differences**, be quick to apologize after the row, **rediscover a different kind of sex life**, give each other space, **count the days together**, don't forget to exercise, **accept the occasional lapse but don't look for it**, use the money you used to spend on dope to treat yourselves to something nice, **save for a holiday**, clean your home, **decorate your home**, dance together, **count your blessings**, challenge yourselves, **learn something new**, open your hearts – to each other and to life itself, **fall in love again.**

Mixed doubles

Tim is an addicted weed smoker he can't have dope in the house without wanting to smoke morning noon and night. Tim wants to quit however because he feels weed is now controlling every aspect of his life. His wife Josie has a more relaxed relationship with cannabis. She like to smoke, but is happy to get high one or two weekends a month. After much discussion they both quit together. All goes well to begin with but after three months Josie says to Tim one Friday night 'I really fancy a smoke what do you think?' Before she has finished the sentence Tim is on the phone to their dealer and an hour or so later they are both stoned. For Josie the occasional weekend of indulgence is just fine, but for Tim, when Monday morning arrives it takes all his strength to throw the remaining bit of skunk away. Two weekends later it's the same scenario, but this time when Monday comes around Tim doesn't throw the dope away he continues smoking, weekday evenings to begin with, and then before they both know it he's back to smoking dope every morning. They try for abstinence one more time but again Josie weakens first, even though she is a recreational smoker she is making abstinence impossible for Tim.

What is the solution?

Realising that he is powerless if dope is in his possession, Tim puts the responsibility for scoring on to Josie. It is Josie's responsibility to buy the cannabis, roll her own joints, smoke when she wishes to and hide the weed from Tim or throw it away when she has had enough. It's Tim's responsibility to either choose to smoke with his wife or not. Not a perfect solution but this way at least they are both taking responsibility for their own needs.

14. Cannabis and Debt

Of course, not everybody who smokes weed on a regular basis gets themselves into financial difficulties, but it can happen; sometimes because we simply have no control over our smoking, which leads us to smoke far more than we can afford. But also because many dope smokers just tend to be experts in the field of not facing up to their problems. And when serious debt does occur, it can be one of the few situations that will allow a Steady stoner to reach their lowest point – in the language of recovery, 'hitting your bottom'.

Toward the end of my dope career I had sold my business and invested in a couple of other ideas that, since I hadn't thought them through, ended up going nowhere. But I was fortunate. I tried for a third time and for a few years found myself supplying bar furniture on a reasonable scale to a major hotel group with locations dotted around the UK. It was simple enough. I was the middle man between a manufacturer and a client who didn't care what else I did, or didn't do, as long as I supplied the goods at the right price and had them assembled on site, and on time. I'd landed on my feet.

I would drive all over the country with a large van full of tables and chairs, and a bag of weed. The difference, or margin, between what the products cost and what I was selling them on for was small, and I was only able to make a living because of the sheer quantity of goods I was selling every month. But as long as I had a roof over my head and enough money for food and dope, I was happy enough.

Eventually I began to take longer payment terms from my suppliers, and built up a bank overdraft just to keep me going in between jobs. Friends advised me to look for other clients, other hotel groups, but I was more interested in finding a new furniture supplier in Amsterdam, as my client had started to open a few hotels in Europe. My profit margin for this European work was even more slight, and my debts grew even bigger. But I didn't care. I just couldn't get enough of the thrill of being my own boss in a foreign city – especially Amsterdam, with its coffee shops and cannabis culture.

As suddenly as it started, the work began to dry up. I soon realized that I was in fairly big trouble. When I looked at my life objectively, I saw someone in his mid-40s living in a rented home, driving a leased car, with no nurturing relationships and some hefty debts. For a long time I had known that my dope smoking was causing me problems of isolation, anxiety and lack of confidence, but now I could also see that my lack of judgement, my refusal to face reality, and my obsession with weed had taken me further and further away from the things that I knew I really wanted in my life – love, security, self-respect and fulfilment. This was my bottom. I'd reached my lowest point, and around this time I began to prepare mentally to say my final goodbyes to cannabis.

The end for me came while on a trip to Berlin to supply chairs. At the time there were only two ferries a week from Harwich, on the Essex coast, to Hamburg, in northern Germany – one on a Sunday and another on a Wednesday. Without fail, I had to be in Berlin by Wednesday, so it was the Sunday ferry I needed to catch.

The day before, I had driven to Wales to pick up the goods. Stoned whilst driving, I had managed to dent the side of my rental van when parking in the factory yard. Nothing serious, but I knew that the repair costs would eat into my already thin profit for the job. So Sunday morning on a freezing cold January day, I'm having my pre-trip joint, sitting in the cab of the van outside my flat in south-east London. As I drive off I notice I've got half a tank of diesel to get me where I'm going. This was in fact more than enough to get me to Harwich and beyond, but somewhere in my clouded mind I decided I needed to fill up sooner rather than later, because – and I don't know where this came from – I thought petrol might be twice the price in Germany.

So I stop off at my local filling station, which I know well. Same old road, same old shops opposite, same old pump; and before I know it, I'm putting in the same old unleaded petrol that I use for my regular car into the tank of the hired van, which only takes diesel fuel. Big mistake. Big stoned mistake. I have a ferry to catch in four hours, and the engine needs to be drained. I know that if I don't get to Berlin by Wednesday I could lose my contract and be out of pocket for this particular job by more money than I want to think about; not to mention my ongoing fears concerning my overdraft and debts.

All I can do is call the truck hire company and ask for a replacement vehicle. This is a Sunday, so I'm not optimistic; in fact, I'm completely freaking out. By some miracle the help-line number for the rental company gets me through to someone who promises to come out with a replacement vehicle within 90 minutes. It was during this time that I made myself a promise – maybe to God, maybe to a higher power, maybe to myself or my unborn children – that if I caught the ferry and made it to Berlin on time I would have finally smoked my last-ever joint.

I took out the bag of weed that I had previously been prepared to smuggle over to Germany and threw it as hard as I could away from me. Of course, this being a wild and windy January day, it flew straight back and almost hit me in the face before nestling in the hood of my coat. To end the story – yes, I did switch the chairs single-handedly from one van to the other. Yes, I did make the ferry to Hamburg, but only just. I was the very last vehicle allowed on, and I had to beg and plead. Yes, I quit smoking and sought help for my addiction. Yes, I ended up with no work and a substantial debt that in many ways I am still paying back years later.

(If you were to ask me today six years later whether I could justify driving a van in the UK and around Europe whilst stoned the answer would be no.)

Ravi, another Clearhead workshop participant, is an example of debt and cannabis problems on a different scale. With no job and no money, he was living on benefits and scraping together small amounts of extra cash by trading on eBay. Every penny he received went toward food and dope. He was in debt to his bank, the local council, and his dealer. A year before, Ravi had an average sort of job, earning average sort of money. Like millions of others, he only just earned enough to survive in the big city. His problem was he was smoking way too much dope, and it was affecting his ability to do his job. He lost perspective and decided that he would quit work, rather than cut back on his smoking. Then his girlfriend left him because he was becoming quite mentally unstable.

Having lost his anchors, he started smoking more and more, to the point where he was doing nothing else. Ravi's family had promised him some money held in trust for him if he was able to get his life back on an even keel, but he had become so reliant on his cannabis smoking, to take away the pain of his situation, that he found it impossible to quit, much as he now wanted to.

Cal, whom I also met through Clearhead, was a self-employed cleaning contractor, and a big-time cannabis smoker who had been systematically defrauding the taxman for rather a long time. He also had many outstanding speeding and parking fines. Cal was in fact an extremely smart and hard-working guy; he also had a lot of insight into his lifestyle. Like so many, he had suffered quite a traumatic childhood, and drugs, especially cannabis, offered short-term answers to deep-rooted problems.

A large part of Cal wanted to sort out his tax problem, but he found himself trapped, as every month his debt to the taxman became more frightening and more unmanageable. Although Cal was earning good money, the idea of finally dealing with the issue seemed increasingly hopeless. It was so much easier to keep smoking and not think about it. Eventually he came to Clearhead and began to turn his life around. He started working weekends, helping out a friend's business, and learnt to live on the extra money he was earning, using his primary income to pay back the taxman.

There are thousands of individuals who, every week, buy weed on credit from their friendly neighbourhood dealer, thus getting caught in a spiral of small-time debt that keeps them hopelessly trapped. For others, even shopping when stoned can warp the judgement. After a few joints have been smoked, it's easy for our thinking to become lazy; to purchase on impulse and deal with the consequences later; to spend more than we can afford; or even to develop 'Jack and the Beanstalk' syndrome, when we're sent out to buy one thing and come back with something completely different.

15. Abstinence v Control

'Nothing in excess – often preached, practised less.'
Clearhead observation

Before we move on to the last two sections, perhaps it's time to consider whether you have control over your dope smoking. For many of us, it can take quite a lot of trial and error to find this out; but for others, to simply notice they are smoking more than they are comfortable with can lead them to pull back and set strict personal limits on when they allow themselves to get stoned.

You may find that you are smoking tobacco joints just to gain a nicotine hit.

You may find that you are spending every hour when you are not smoking in discomfort, waiting to get home or to a safe place to get stoned.

You may find that you are bored with smoking all the time but find it difficult to think of anything else you would rather be doing.

You may find that all the usual things you like to do when you are stoned have absolutely no interest to you when you are straight.

Does agreement to these scenarios mean you are addicted to cannabis, or could you learn to control your use? This is for you to decide.

Some people instinctively know that they cannot smoke dope with any control. It's all or nothing for them. As they say in the 12-Step Programme, 'One joint/line/drink is never enough – one is too many.'

Maybe you have decided you are a heavy smoker and that's the way you like it. I hold no judgement. As far as I'm concerned, it's your mind and body, to do what you like with, but don't rule out the possibility of change. Change is happening all the time. Circumstances change, our health changes, our responsibilities change, along with our beliefs and attitudes. Leave the door open. Remember, you only have one life that you are absolutely sure about, and this is it! Smoking dope all the time is like eating the same three meals every day. "Live a little", as my late grandfather used to say.

Perhaps you are ready to do a deal with yourself and are going to try to control your use. In my experience, it is more realistic to practise only smoking with others and not by yourself, rather than saying I will only smoke on weekends or evenings.

If, after reading this far, you have come to the conclusion you *are* addicted, I want to tell you sincerely that there is no shame in being an addict. All sorts of people become addicted to all sorts of substances and behaviours for all sorts of reasons. Perhaps you are lucky that you chose cannabis as your drug of choice, rather than something even more unhealthy or indeed dangerous. More than that, perhaps you are lucky to have reached a point where you are considering making some positive changes.

Of course, this is a daunting prospect; but on the other hand, isn't there another part of you that is weirdly excited?

There are those in the 'cannabis is basically harmless, legalize it now' camp who say that cannabis addiction is primarily a process of wanting to repeat an enjoyable experience, simply because it is enjoyable. This is only part of the story. The true addict has reached a tolerance level at which they experience withdrawal when they are not stoned. For some people this only lasts a few days; for others, usually those of us who have been smoking more, for longer, it's a longer process. But either way; you need to resolutely break through the discomfort barrier and get to the other side. And this will be much easier to do after you have read the final two sections of this book.

Some of the ideas in this book will need to be thought about deeply. A few may come as a revelation to you, whilst I am sure you will also find things to disagree with. But for goodness sake, don't let pride, or indeed a feeling of hope-lessness, stop you from taking control of your own life again, whether it's through control or abstinence. If you are still not sure whether you want to stop smoking finally and forever, or even if you are capable of it, that's okay.

If you are torn between a desire for positive change and a real fear of never smoking cannabis ever again, I can understand your position. Perhaps what you are experi-encing can best be described as a fear of your own potential, your own power. Even if you are a parent yourself, I would suggest that you have been keeping some part of your own childhood or adolescence hidden inside a cloud of smoke. Maybe you like that part of yourself and don't want to lose it. But in the final analysis, if cannabis is holding you back … Relax. Perhaps now is the time to prove to yourself that you can quit if you want to. To allow some new life choices. My advice to you would be to commit to quitting for three months, see how you feel at that time, and then re-read the final section of this book.

Section 3 Starting to Stop

16. Preparation

'Positive belief at the start of a doubtful undertaking is often the one thing ensuring success.'
William James, 1842-1910, American Psychologist

Those of us who possess the addictive gene are not known for our patience, or our planning skills. Usually, when we want something, we want it now. When we want to get high, we want to get high right now. Not tomorrow, not next week, but *now*.

Likewise, when we finally decide that we are ready to make positive changes in relation to our addiction, we want to start right away, while we are in a strong frame of mind. It is, of course, vital to retain this positive momentum, but it's also important to remember that putting the brakes on any habit, let alone an addiction that has been built up over a period of years, is a process that needs planning. We should also be aware that sometimes our addictive impulses are so strong that even as we contemplate change our negative subconscious is already planning ways to self-sabotage the process. So to give ourselves the best chance of success, it makes sense to clear the path ahead by being mindful of the potential problems and obstacles that might stop us achieving the freedom from active addiction we are looking for.

Confidence

When breaking any habit or addictive behaviour, it's only natural to have doubts as to your ability to succeed. Perhaps you've tried before with the best of intentions, only to end up back where you started. It's important to recognize that every attempt is unique, and that if you are worried that you will fail in the same way as you have done previously, this is completely unfounded in reality. You will have learnt valuable lessons from your past experiences, so, rather than being doomed to repeat the mistakes of the past, this time, with the help of this book, there is every reason to expect you will be able to beat this problem once and for all.

You are of course bound to feel apprehensive about your ability to succeed. This is because you yourself realize that the stakes are high. Quitting is something you've probably been thinking about for some time, and to actually start the process feels like a big test as to your own personal ability to achieve the things that you want in your life. Self-doubt is part of the process, and it's not unusual at this stage to be conflicted between clearly seeing how your excessive smoking is damaging both yourself and your relationships, whilst still having concerns because you retain elements of pleasure from being stoned.

Perhaps your cannabis smoking has become such an ingrained habit, such a huge part of your life, that you can barely imagine an existence without weed. Don't worry, thousands of others have also been at that very place and yet have managed to change things round to the point where they are no longer obsessed with, or act compulsively, around cannabis. How have they managed to make the break? What is the secret of their success?

Acceptance

One simple answer lies in acceptance. A final acceptance of the nature of your cannabis addiction, beyond what you have wanted to believe for years about dope and you – its soft drug status, its medicinal benefits, its recreational qualities. This very acceptance offers some hard, but in a way quite simple, choices.

If not now, when?

It's surprising how many smokers I've spoken to share this same fantasy. They see themselves elderly and retired, no longer burdened by work or family responsibilities, perhaps sitting in a fantasy comfy chair, in a fantasy garden. The sky is blue, the sun is out – it's a perfect spring morning. One or two, possibly three, ready-rolled joints sit on a table alongside an ashtray, a lighter and your music player. Perhaps a few chilled drinks in an ice bucket complete the picture. Nothing to do this morning but get stoned.

What's wrong with this picture?

The problem with this particular fantasy is that it gives us permission to smoke dope and get stoned whenever we want, without negative consequence – something that for most people in their everyday lives just isn't sustainable. In reality, will we ever reach the point where we will be at ease with a part of ourselves that takes up so much emotional energy to service?

Also, does our cannabis consumption continue to feed our physical energy? If we sometimes feel tired and confused when we're stoned at the age we are now, how will we feel as we approach our later years? Will our memory start to miraculously improve? Will we suddenly find astonishing new reserves of energy as the years go by? No, of course we won't. As we grow older we need to take more care of ourselves physically, instead of spending every day with our minds and bodies out of balance with each other.

Personal growth

As soon as we begin to take steps away from our comfort zone toward doing things that we don't want to do, we are learning to harness our personal power.

Addicts tend to be selfish, often unmindful of the needs of others. We may think of ourselves as kind, loving individuals, but at the end of the day, we don't like to let anything or anybody get in the way of our fix.

Many of us have demeaned ourselves through our need to get high, by associating with people we have no respect for, or who have no respect for us. Some of our actions and attitudes may have been questionable. Is it possible that if we could just break the cycle of addiction we might finally begin to fulfil our highest potential, even if that means nothing more than to reach a truer level of contentment and happiness?

Later in this section we are going to run a trial for a short while by starting to monitor and delay your desire to smoke. Remember when we first started to experiment with smoking dope, how we had to learn, through trial and error, which situations were uncomfortable to be stoned in for example, or to not put too much grass or hash in a joint because we couldn't handle it? Well, in a way, starting to quit is a similar process. We have to experiment again with our tolerance level to find out how many joints we really **need** to smoke, and how many are simply out of habit.

Tobacco joints

Before you start to monitor your dope smoking, if you smoke tobacco with your cannabis it's important to realize that your desire for a joint may simply be masking an urgent need for a nicotine fix. The sad truth is that tobacco joints are a highly addictive cocktail. Our craving for cannabis essentially feels like a strong desire to turn off our minds from everyday reality. Our craving for nicotine, on the other hand, feels like a deep physical hunger in the pit of our stomach.

As you start the process of quitting, it's crucial to begin to recognize and separate the two cravings. If you are committed to quitting cannabis then it's a safe bet that you do not want to exchange cannabis addiction with nicotine addiction. But if you have been smoking tobacco joints regularly for any length of time, I'm afraid you are almost certainly a hardened nicotine addict, even if you have never smoked a cigarette in your life.

People who don't understand how addictive cannabis is will tell you that it's much easier to give up dope than it is nicotine. I wish it was as simple as that, but it's not. Over the years I have been doing this work, I have met some people who have been able to quit both tobacco and cannabis at the same time, but I've known just as many who when attempting to quit both together have found themselves back at square one in a moment of weakness. There is much more information on this subject in the next section of the book, which focuses on helping you through the adjustment period, but for now I just want you to practise separating the two cravings as you begin to monitor your dope smoking.

Monitoring your intake

Over the following days or weeks, as you read through the chapters of this book, I want you to experiment with becoming super-conscious of how you are using cannabis, and to notice how so often it's effects can end up using you. Let's think about what you are actually getting out of smoking weed at this point. Is it giving you the same buzz as you got in the early days? Or are you in fact just smoking to normalize? Not to get high or even feel good but just to stop yourself feeling uncomfortable and empty.

Start to experiment with not smoking immediately you get a craving, or when it's your usual time to spark up. If you smoke by yourself, do something else instead. Have a shower or bath, go for a quick walk, make yourself a snack, wash the dishes, check your emails, read a few chapters of a book. Even if these were activities you used to undertake with a joint in your hand, the idea is to distract yourself for a few minutes. You will notice that while you are focused on some other small activity, the desire to smoke lessens or, for a moment or two, disappears completely.

Carry out this exercise regularly for two weeks, safe in the knowledge that you can smoke at any time. Remember, the choice, as ever, belongs to you.

You will probably find that, at the very beginning of this experiment, your mind will find it hard to focus or concentrate on what it is doing, constantly coming back to 'I want a joint'. This is not a time to immediately give in to your mind. Every time you resist the call of a joint you are building up your mental discipline.

Start off, during the first week, by distracting yourself for half an hour. Remember, a craving only lasts as long as you indulge it. Do this as often as you can every day. Get used to reclaiming some power over your mind. Sometimes your inner voice will tell you that this time it doesn't matter and you are not going to wait, the need to smoke is just too strong. This is the time to be extra-determined. Dig deep to go that half an hour. Notice whether it is nicotine or cannabis you are craving. Remember to consistently acknowledge yourself for the strength of character you are showing. You should quite literally repeat your name out loud and tell yourself how well you are doing.

After a while you will feel so comfortable that smoking again after only half an hour would seem silly. Why spoil your sense of satisfaction by giving in so easily? This is the time to resolve to go for another half an hour. When you reach seven full days of this practice, you can begin to step up your delaying tactics. This second week, delay your need for THC gratification for one hour and a half, or even longer if you can. Once more, do this throughout your normal times of smoking, particularly if you usually smoke alone.

Challenge yourself. For example, if you normally smoke a joint whilst watching a favourite TV programme, don't this time. Wait until it's finished, or well in to the next show before you light up. Notice how your mind nags that you are missing out by not being stoned to the max at this precise time. So what? Remind yourself that through these tiny bits of discomfort you are paving the way to break free of a dependency that has kept you trapped for a long time. Millions of people watch that very same TV show without being under the influence of drugs or alcohol, never even thinking about anything else but enjoying what they are watching.

When you do allow yourself to smoke, notice how it makes you feel as you begin to get stoned. Do you feel light or heavy, relaxed or agitated, insightful or blank, tight or loose? Don't *judge* how you're feeling, just make a quick note.

Next, monitor your contentment level. I want you to specifically mark it out of three:

1 = Made me feel either tired, restless or anxious.
2 = Just another joint.
3 = Made what I was doing better; made me feel good.

Draw up a table like the one below. Make some copies and use it as much as you can every day.

Day	Time
Feeling	
Contentment level	

To start with, this little exercise will allow you to honestly and accurately work out how many joints you are smoking through the day and evening. Many dope smokers smoke small joints with tobacco, almost like cigarettes. Is this what you are doing? Others will smoke a larger joint, either shared with friends or all by themselves over a period of time.

If you are doing this exercise properly, you may well find there are plenty of 3s in your contentment level, but this should be because you are building spaces between your initial desire for a smoke and the time you actually allow yourself to have one.

My partner or family member smokes, or I am in a social situation

If people who are close to you in your life are continuing to smoke, you may believe that this exercise is going to be harder for you; but it doesn't have to be.

If it's your partner, for example, explain what you are doing. There's a good chance they will support you by joining you in this experiment. After all, you're not asking them to quit themselves, only to cut down their cannabis intake for a couple of weeks as you yourself prepare to quit.

If they are determined to continue smoking at their own pace, they may still be supportive enough to not smoke in the same room as you while you go through this exercise of slowly but surely building your personal willpower. If they won't support you even by helping you in this way, then now is not the time to get emotional or angry with them. Channel any negative feelings you may have about the situation into making yourself even more determined to quit by yourself, for yourself.

If you find yourself in regular social situations where there is always weed about, whether in a bong, pipe or joint, stay calm. Smoke, but not as rapidly as you normally would. Try to appreciate the buzz you have, rather than continually chasing the desire to get even higher just because the opportunity is there. Again, slowly start to regain control over your instinctive desire to smoke everything that is put in front of you. Begin to analyse how being stoned in a group of people makes you feel. Look around you and start to consider whether this sort of ongoing social situation is really fun anymore. Is it offering you the opportunities for change and growth that you deserve in your life?

Sleep-over

If your pattern is to stay up late and smoke, or you believe that you need to smoke heavily or have a bedtime joint to send you off to sleep, try for one or two nights – perhaps around the weekend, on a Friday or a Saturday, when you know you don't have to get up early the next morning to have your last intake of cannabis three hours prior to going to bed. You can still smoke in the evening, but try not to drink coffee or alcohol after 6 p.m. You may well have some resistance to this experiment but look on it as a positive change of habit rather that something that fills you with dread.

Perhaps you might even want to get to bed a little earlier than usual. Take some care over your bedtime routine. Have a pre-bed bath; use scented candles, oils, or incense to create a relaxing, soothing atmosphere (especially you guys out there); change your bedding; and if you have purchased the Clearhead recording use it to help you drop off. Just do things differently. If you find it difficult to sleep immediately because of this experimental change of routine, don't panic. Allow yourself to rest, knowing that you don't have to rush to get up the next morning. If you still wake up a few times during the night, stay calm. Make sure you have a good book to read until you start to feel tired and doze off again. (For many more tips on sleep, see the next section.)

Reflecting on Mr and Ms Weed

As you continue this process and begin to think deeply about your relationship with cannabis, now is the time to consider that what you are doing is preparing to say goodbye to a lover or an old friend. Let's call him Mr Weed.

Everybody has their own version of Mr Weed. Mine is actually Ms Weed, a lady of a certain age who seduced me when I was 15 and young enough not to know any better. At first I was flattered by her attentions. She used to dance with me the old-fashioned way. She held me tight, day after day, night after night, for weeks, months and years on end. As she got older and she lost her looks, her grip became tighter until, try as I might, I couldn't release myself.

At first I thought she loved me; she told me I didn't have to be lonely as long as she was with me. The years began to go by so quickly, and our love affair turned into a marriage. I began to worry about having gotten into such a serious relationship at such a young age, and although I felt trapped, I couldn't imagine a life without her, even though her embrace was cold and the age difference was really beginning to kick in. She was now an old lady. Sometimes when we danced it felt like I was holding a skeleton attached to a ball and chain.

Perhaps your version of Mr Weed is a best mate, a wild friend who made every occasion more fun, more of a laugh than it ever actually was, until …

Or maybe a fabulously creative musician or artist who used to give you wonderful inspiration and great ideas, but then…

Possibly he was the coolest looking guy/girl at school, drop-dead-gorgeous looks but not really very bright …

You get the idea. Actually, in some weird way it's kind of helpful to think of weed as a separate entity. After all, when I was smoking, my relationship with cannabis was more important to me than my family, my friends, life itself. But now is the time to reflect on *your* relationship with Mr/Ms Weed. If it helps, write some stuff down. But you don't have to. Simply put, the idea of this exercise is for you to consider how your relationship with weed has slowly changed over the years; how something you loved dearly and trusted implicitly turned around until it began to completely dominate all areas of your life.

'Dear John' letter

Perhaps this is the time for a few short lines of goodbye to John or Joan Weed '… I love you, but you're killing me'; 'we can't go on like this'; 'I want my life back'; 'you've taken so much from me', etc. Nobody has to see this but you. Write a few lines, even if to begin with it seems silly. Write as much as you can, put it away and keep it for a few days, then re-read what you have written. You can then burn it, chuck it away or keep it. The important thing is to truly feel what you have written is true.

To further examine how weed is impacting on your life, here is a simple multiple-choice form for you to complete. It goes without saying that, to obtain an objective perspective, you need to be totally honest with yourself. Use a pencil to tick the appropriate answer. After you have finished, leave it for a few days and then have another look over it, making whatever changes necessary. Think about what you have learnt.

Age started smoking …

Age now …

How long been smoking …

Do you smoke every day?

Yes ☐

No ☐

Just weekends ☐

Do you prefer to smoke skunk?

Yes ☐

No ☐

Whenever I can get it ☐

Given the choice between polluted low-grade dope and
nothing, I would smoke … ☐

Low-grade dope ☐

Wait for something better tomorrow ☐

Do you smoke in the morning?

Yes ☐

No ☐

Just weekends ☐

Do you smoke more than you did a year ago?

Yes ☐

No ☐

The same ☐

Do you believe you need to smoke before sleeping?

    Yes   ☐

    No   ☐

How do you sleep?

    Badly   ☐

    Quite well   ☐

    Very well   ☐

Do you believe you need to smoke to fully relax?

    Yes   ☐

    No   ☐

How would you describe your energy level?

    Consistently strong   ☐

    Low   ☐

    Variable   ☐

Do you smoke mainly …

    By yourself   ☐

    With others   ☐

    Both   ☐

How much do you spend on weed every month?   ….

    (please be extra honest here)

Do you think smoking makes your life?

     More boring ☐

     More interesting ☐

     Bearable ☐

Do you find you are smoking when you could be doing other things?

     Yes ☐

     No ☐

Do you find you are smoking when you *should* be doing other things?

     Yes ☐

     No ☐

Do you consider yourself a disciplined person?

     Yes ☐

     No ☐

     Sometimes ☐

     About everything other than weed ☐

Do you think you are a reliable person?

     Yes ☐

     No ☐

     Only when I haven't smoked ☐

Do you think you are a happy person?

    Most of the time ☐

    Some of the time ☐

    Quite unhappy ☐

Do you like yourself?

    Yes ☐

    No ☐

    Most of the time ☐

    Not like I used to ☐

    Not sure ☐

Do you think other people respect you?

    Generally, yes ☐

    Some people some of the time ☐

    No ☐

Do you consider yourself …

    Social ☐

    Quite Shy ☐

    Prefer my own company or those I know really
well ☐

When your supply of cannabis is running low, do you …

    Start to feel slightly anxious ☐

    Feel really concerned until you score again ☐

If ever you run out for any reason, are/do you …

Irritable ☐

Angry ☐

Unable to concentrate ☐

Think now is a good time to quit ☐

Are you prone to depression?

Yes ☐

No ☐

Do you take medication for your depression?

Yes ☐

No ☐

Irregularly ☐

Do you suffer from panic attacks?

Yes ☐

No ☐

Never ☐

Do you get paranoid about people or situations?

Regularly ☐

Sometimes ☐

Never ☐

Do you feel trapped by your smoking?

Yes ☐

No ☐

Do you think it would be possible to give up tobacco whilst still smoking weed?

      Yes ☐

      No ☐

      Don't smoke tobacco ☐

Does smoking stop you exercising as regularly as you feel you should?

      Yes ☐

      No ☐

Ever suffer breathlessness?

      Often ☐

      Occasionally ☐

      Once or twice ☐

Ever suffer rapid heartbeat?

      Often ☐

      Occasionally ☐

      Once or twice ☐

How would you describe your diet?

      Very healthy ☐

      Quite healthy ☐

      Generally unhealthy ☐

Do you drink alcohol?

Regularly ☐

Occasionally ☐

Hardly ever/Never ☐

Do you like to mix cannabis with alcohol?

Yes ☐

No ☐

How many times have you thrown a whitey (blacked out) in the last?

Month ... ☐

Year ... ☐

Have you used other recreational drugs during ...

The last six months ☐

The last three months ☐

The last six weeks ☐

Do you consider cannabis to be your first drug of choice?

Yes ☐

No ☐

Do you find it difficult to get out of bed in the morning?

Usually ☐

Sometimes ☐

Leap out ☐

Has cannabis ever stopped you finding work?

    Yes ☐

    No ☐

Do you smoke at work?

    Regularly ☐

    Sometimes ☐

    Never ☐

Would you be in trouble if your employer knew you
smoked dope out of work hours?

    Yes ☐

    No ☐

    Self-employed ☐

Does smoking affect your work/studies?

    Positively ☐

    Negatively ☐

    Not sure ☐

Are you married or have a live-in relationship?

    Yes ☐

    No ☐

Do you have a partner?

    Yes ☐

    No ☐

Do they smoke?

     Yes   ☐

     No   ☐

Does your dope smoking cause friction?

     Yes   ☐

     No   ☐

Have you ever smoked dope with your parents?

     Yes   ☐

     No   ☐

     They don't know I smoke   ☐

Do you feel guilty about your cannabis smoking?

     Most of the time   ☐

     Some of the time   ☐

     Not really   ☐

Are you constantly trying to quit?

     Yes   ☐

     No   ☐

What do you want, what do you really, really want?

Well, what are the things you want in life that smoking weed is getting in the way of?

Again, it's crucial to be totally honest with yourself as to your long-term motivation for needing to make positive changes around your cannabis smoking. The best way to think clearly about your personal goals is to write down some of the things that motivated you to reach this point.

For example, you might write something like this:

I want to stop smoking weed because

It's bad for my health.

It's a waste of money.

I feel guilty because I know I *should* be stopping.

It makes me anti-social, so I miss out on stuff.

It's hard to focus when I'm stoned, etc.

Or

It's shit.

It makes me crazy.

It gives me mood swings.

It steals my energy.

It makes me paranoid, etc.

Others might write something like this:

I'm married to dope. This causes ongoing relationship problems. The continual cycle of getting stoned and trying to quit is doing my head in. I want to know the truth about who I am and what I think about things, etc.

Now is the time for *you* to write *your* motivation.

Make this an ongoing process over a few days. Don't be surprised if some of your strongest motivations for change come to you when you're stoned. Just write them all down, day or night, starting like this:

I want to stop smoking cannabis because ...

After two or three days you should have quite a list. It doesn't matter if they're small reasons or if you see them as being highly significant, they all go toward creating a whole, a picture of what led you to this point. When you have written as much as you think you are ever going to write, copy your motivations down one more time on a brand new piece of paper, either typed or in your best handwriting.

Why do I need to write it out again? I've already done it once!

This information is important. Treat it with respect. These are not just words on paper, this is real. This is the reality of your life. It's a reality that you probably haven't shared much with others, if ever. In fact, it's probably one of the most important bits of paper you may ever have in your possession. The act of writing it again allows you to examine, one more time, your commitment to these changes.

Next, based on what you have already written, write a short positive visualization of how your life might be in 12 months' time, having not smoked weed for this period.

It is now … (Today's date + one year ahead). I haven't smoked weed for 12 months, life is now different because …

Your visualization might look something like this:
I come home and feel comfortable in my surroundings. I am stable and confident and not led by my emotions. I can see more clearly, I'm more in control, more centred, less moody. I can have fun and now enjoy life to the full, without the need to smoke maintaining the illusion that I am making everything better all of the time.

Or it could look something like this …
I am not so scared anymore. I am happier, and less anxious about people and situations. I am actually proud to be the person I am again. I have drive and motivation back in my life.

Or this …
I am more sociable. I visit friends more often, or go out for drinks with people at work, rather than rushing home to get stoned by myself all of the time. I no longer feel detached from what is going on around me. I am now enjoying natural sleep and feel much less tired.

Again, write this visualization out once more. Write as much as you can, and make sure it looks immaculate – and keep it that way. Treat this bit of paper the same as your motivational piece. Treat it with respect. As you approach your quitting day, put both pieces of paper where you know you will see them every day. Make extra copies, for your handbag or briefcase, as you go through those crucial early days of quitting.

Finally, take a deep breath and decide on a quitting day. Monday is traditionally a better day for quitting than a Friday. Perhaps you might want to choose the first day of the month. If you still feel really unsure that you are ready, move your quitting day one week ahead (you can only do this once). Some people will find their smoking increases greatly as quitting day approaches; others will find that, by following the procedures in this chapter, their smoking is tapering off nicely. However it's going, don't quit before your designated quitting day, and save some dope for your last smoke.

Checklist
Prepare yourself for quitting by:
Finally accepting that cannabis is an addictive drug that has more control over you, than you do over it.

Being totally honest as to the negative impact your everyday cannabis smoking has on different areas of

your life, such as work, relationships and your confidence.

Understanding fully that everyday cannabis use and a healthy lifestyle are not mutually compatible.

Experimenting with not smoking as soon as you get a craving. (You may feel that this part of the process is enough and that now you are back in control of your consumption. Don't be fooled. At this stage you need to put real distance between you and cannabis to break your dependency)

Noticing and recording how cannabis makes you feel immediately after you've had a smoke, and how you use this time.

Practising a change of your nightly routine to accommodate missing out on your bedtime smoke.

If you have purchased the Clearhead hypnotherapy recording, start to listen to it to help you relax naturally and let go of any immediate urgent cravings for cannabis.

Filling out the form to understand more fully your relationship with cannabis.

Writing your motivation for quitting smoking. How is cannabis stopping you achieving your goals and potential?

Writing your visualization as to how you see your life in 12 months' time, having not smoked cannabis in that period.

Making pristine copies of your motivation and visualization statements, then putting them somewhere around the house where you will see them. Make copies to take with you to refer to during the day.

Choose a quitting day and stick to it!

17. Quitting Day

'Action expresses priorities.'
Mahatma Gandhi

Perhaps you've made attempts at quitting cannabis before. It's not unusual for some people to make multiple attempts before being successful; others are able to find the mental strength required on their first attempt. It doesn't matter whether this is your first or thousandth attempt. What is important is that this time you prioritize your decision. For the moment, this time is the only time that counts.

Action expresses priorities. You've taken the action – you're using this book, you've analysed your relationship with weed, you understand clearly why it's time to stop and what benefits you want for yourself. All of this certainly shows a real level of commitment that will serve you well, but I want you to think carefully for a moment about how important it really is for you to achieve your goal.

Is quitting:
More important than your job?

More important than your relationship, your marriage or your family?

More important than your friendships, your image, or even simply getting a good night's sleep?

Actually, for the next two months, I would suggest to you that it is.

You may be thinking, *How could giving up weed be more important than my family? These are the most important people in my life.*

I know many people who have reached the point of quitting cannabis because they are concerned about the quality of the relationship they have with their children, their partners and close family.

Howard is the father of two girls, aged eight and eleven, and he found it increasingly hard to keep the fact that he used cannabis from them as they grew older. They thought he was a cigarette smoker, which was bad enough. The oldest had been taught about the evils of all drugs from her PHSE teacher at school, and would have been upset to find out that her dad smoked dope. But, of course, on some level she did know. His kids might not have been able to express it, but the truth was that, although physically present, he would sometimes seem distant, distracted. Often, too often, he would be irritable with them for reasons they couldn't understand (he was irritable, of course, because he couldn't smoke whilst they were around).

Angie had a different problem. As a cannabis user herself, for two years she had accepted that her 17-year-old son Martin was also toking joints; sometimes they would smoke together, and, to her shame, she occasionally borrowed the odd spliff from him when she ran out. She constantly felt guilty because she could see how Martin's smoking was affecting his exam prospects, and yet she couldn't say anything because of her own weed addiction.

Ed came to Clearhead having recently split up with a long-term girlfriend. He admitted that his relationship with weed was stronger, far stronger, than the one with his girlfriend, and she had finally got fed up with the lack of energy and passion he showed in keeping the relationship alive.

Daniel worked in sales. For years smoking weed had been his way of escaping from the intense pressures of his job. But slowly his judgement began to become less reliable. His personality changed from being a genuinely considerate person to having to pretend to be friendly, putting on an act to hide his paranoia and anxiety from clients and work colleagues. His real fear was that if he couldn't get his cannabis fix he wouldn't be able to function at his job properly. He had tried to quit once before and suffered sleep disruption to the point where he couldn't concentrate properly at work.

Whom should I tell? Finding support

Many of us find it hard enough to admit to ourselves that our dope smoking is causing us problems, therefore it's understandable that when we are planning to quit we are careful about whom we tell. We might worry that our smoking buddies won't understand what all the fuss is about; perhaps they might laugh at us or not take our concerns seriously. Actually, in my experience, it can be other smokers who are often, but not always, the most supportive. Why? Because only another addicted dope smoker truly understands the hold that weed can have over us. Even smokers who see no reason to quit themselves know that at different times their smoking has caused them problems. Many will support your efforts. There will be others, of course, who feel threatened by your decision, as it upsets their conception of who you are, and this may force them to question their own relationship with cannabis.

The important thing is to find quality support from as many people as you can. I know some who, upon quitting, told everybody they knew – smokers and non-smokers alike. This approach works well for some people, but for others it piles on too much pressure at an early stage. Although you may feel you have the personality type that thrives on this sort of challenge, do you really want to be so open about your private life to all-comers? It could be better to sound people out, people you know and trust. Here are a few scenarios.

Your very best smoking buddy: Will often be most supportive. Even though you are talking about breaking a strong bond, they will respect your decision because the bond of friendship is stronger than the bond of drugs. hopefully they will understand that, for the moment, it won't be a good idea for them to smoke dope when you are around. This might mean just catching up by text, phone or email for a while, rather than meeting up as often as you are used to. If they do come round, or they invite you over, remind them that, for the moment, it's difficult for you to be around people smoking.

When my friend Anne quit she made her home a smoke-free zone. Unfortunately, her neighbour was also her smoking buddy. To begin with, her neighbour was irritated, because her habit was to nip round to Anne's and share a smoke when her kids were asleep. She started being sarcastic about Anne's new regime, but Anne was resolute and the neighbour finally saw that if she wanted to retain any sort of friendship she would have to accept that things had changed.

Friends and acquaintances: Everybody is different. Some of your friends will be supportive, others will be defensive. A good move might be to tell those you don't think will understand the issue that you are just taking a break from cannabis for a while. That way you are taking the pressure off yourself. One of my colleagues at Clearhead has a much more direct attitude. She is happy to tell anybody that asks the reason she doesn't smoke weed anymore was because for 15 years she used to have a smoke every morning before she even got out of bed.

The truth is that by quitting you are making an important life-changing decision about who you are, and that of course impacts on how you spend your time, and with whom. I understand what it's like to live in a town or village where everybody knows everybody else, and for most kids the only youth culture is drug culture. Some of your friends from school will have graduated to hard drug use, where smoking weed doesn't even register as part of their thinking. Others will be dealers; still others are people you have been drinking and smoking with for years. But there will also be one or two who have settled down, having quit smoking dope some time ago. Seek them out, begin to ask them their reasons for quitting, and tell them of your plans. They will be only too pleased to offer the benefit of their experience.

Significant others: They say no one really knows what goes on within somebody else's relationship, and this is of course true. There are thousands of couples who smoke together, sometimes happily. An alternative scenario is that in which one or the other partner is constantly trying to quit. I would say it's quite rare for both to be ready to quit at the same time, though it does happen. The important thing to remember is that you are separate people with separate motivations, and that you are quitting for yourself and not your partner.

Pete and Sandra had been married for over 25 years, and had smoked together for as long as they'd known each other. They used to have friendly arguments about who smoked the most. Sandra worked from home and looked after the kids. She would smoke all day, from breakfast to last thing at night; not big joints, just little skinny ones to keep her buzz topped up all day. Pete would come home in the evening, after work, and roll giant spliffs for himself in order to 'unwind'. He would smoke till one or two in the morning. When eventually they figured out who was smoking the most, it worked out that they were smoking exactly the same amount.

Sandra eventually quit, after 30 years' hardcore smoking, with the help of her local drug agency. Pete quit cold turkey, with no external support, a while later, when he felt he was ready. They both had different ways of dealing with the issue, which reflected the different people that they are.

Parents and close family: It can be particularly hard to share with our parents and close family the fact that cannabis has become a problem for us. Perhaps they don't even know that you smoke; possibly they thought you gave up years ago; or maybe they even got you started in the first place.

Caleb, found an article about Clearhead placed on his desk at home by his dad, who just said, "It's not for you, but some of your friends may find this interesting." Caleb came on the weekend, insisting that his dad had no idea he smoked dope. In fact, your parents and close family will probably offer the most supportive help. You might think they will be angry that you have run into problems with weed; you may think that they won't understand. But no matter what happened in the past, your parents (or parent) even if they smoke themselves, will usually be very proud that you are making this positive change in your life.

Support is vital. It can mean the difference between success and failure. Don't go into your first day weed-free without at least one other person you can turn to with complete confidence for support.

Other preparations – can you make your home a weed-free environment?

This is definitely a good idea, but realistically it is not always possible, as our home mates and loved ones may still be smoking. At the very least, if the people you share your home with are continuing to smoke, they need to be respectful of you and your choices. That means: no mucking around, no joking, no testing or teasing. You need to make sure others are in no doubt of your commitment to this effort.

If you find yourself living in a shared home where the living room is a smoking room, you need to think carefully about how to make the best of the situation, which may actually involve checking out the flat-share ads in the local paper for a new place to live before you commit to a quitting day. Drastic, I know, but remember what I said at the beginning of the chapter about prioritizing your decision? For the next few months, not smoking weed is going to be more important than your living arrangements.

On the other hand, if you are sharing with one or two other smokers who occasionally smoke in the living room, tell them of your plans and request they don't smoke in your face. Nine times out of ten, they will be entirely supportive of your decision.

Make your own room the nicest it's ever been. Keep it well ventilated, make an effort to keep it clean and tidy, change the bed-linen regularly, and spend some of the money you will not be spending on weed to buy some nice things which will make your room a special and welcoming place for you to call home.

If you find yourself living with others who you know are still smoking but are now no longer smoking in front of you, it may prove worthwhile to study their behaviour closely. Do they look like they've been having a good time? Do they seem alert, or even fully awake? Do they understand what you are saying, or do you constantly find that you are having to repeat yourself? Are they positive, or do you notice that they seem quite defensive, detached, or even depressed much of the time? Again, I'm not saying that smoking dope has negative consequences for all of us all of the time. Everybody makes their own choices in life, but it's amazing what insight a little bit of distance can give.

If you're in the lucky position where your home is your own, then make it a weed-free zone for yourself, obviously, but also to visitors and guests. Additionally, think about how you can change things in a positive way, whether by redecorating or by shifting the furniture to create a changed environment. Your first day without weed marks the start of a new life. Much that happened yesterday was habitual, boring and predictable. When you begin to leave cannabis dependency behind, life can seem strange as your mind adjusts to the fact that it isn't stoned anymore. Changing your living space gives your mind something else to think about, another aspect of life that feels unfamiliar, as well as positive and exciting.

What about my dealer(s)?

The truth is, not many people feel confident enough at this stage to delete their dealers' numbers from their mobile phones. But if you are ready to do so, go ahead. Your dealer may be a good friend who will actually support you in your decision; or he or she might just see you as a customer who offers a guaranteed weekly income. Perhaps you are a dealer yourself. For a while I used to score my weed from a guy who gave up years before I ever met him. I could never understand where he was coming from at the time. I do now.

Things to do before quitting day checklist

Prioritize your decision to quit. It's almost certainly the most important decision you will make this year.

Mentally prepare yourself for some physical withdrawal. Don't fear it, welcome it.

Tell the people you trust of your decision to quit. You can tell others that you are just taking a break for a while. Take the decision not to be around smokers until you feel ready.

Be clear with your significant other about what you are doing and why.

Make at least part of your home a smoke-free zone. Ask for a level of support from the people you live with.

Commit to decorating your living space, or at least moving the furniture around. Buy some nice stuff for your home, even if it's small items like candles or incense or new bed linen.

Commit to keeping your living space as tidy as possible.

Delete your dealers' numbers from your phone.

If you have purchased the Clearhead hypnotherapy record-ing, continue using it to ease the cravings, relax naturally, and help you sleep.

18. Your Last Smoke

'Do not dwell in the past, do not dream of the future. Concentrate the mind on the present moment.'
Buddha

How many joints, pipes, buckets or bongs have you smoked in your life? A thousand? Ten thousand? Does it even matter? Not really, but how your lungs feel every morning could probably give you a good indication.

It's now time to prepare for your last smoking session. Perhaps this is something you have done or thought about many times before. It's really best not to place any kind of special significance on these last few smokes. Truly, they're no different from the thousands of other sessions that you've had with dope over the years. Is this really going to be your last smoke ever? No need to think in those terms. My advice would be to simply consider the next 24 hours without smoking as a real achievement. Remember, even at this point there's always choice at every stage of the process. But for now it's okay just to say something like, "I've had enough. I'm through with it. I'm not even enjoying it anymore. I've done this for such a long time, and I want more positive things in my life."

Before, during or after your last smoking session, I want you to start preparing to throw some stuff out before you go to bed that night. If you've tried to quit before, chances are that you've been through the ritual of chucking out your paraphernalia. And it **is** a ritual, in the same way that every time you score, skin up a joint and have your first smoke from a brand new stash is a ritual. In the same way that you have your own special way of rolling joints, and your favourite special places and times to smoke. These are all smoking rituals, and now this is your quitting ritual.

It's time to chuck away everything associated with your smoking. Please try and make sure you save a small amount of dope, just enough for a tiny joint, to chuck away as well. Throwing this last bit away signifies your strength of purpose. Now is also the time to throw away any specialist cigarette papers, pipes, bongs, lighters, etc. Oh, and chuck your stash box away while you're at it.

What? I don't have to throw that away, as well, do I?
Why not? It's amazing what symbolic value we place on the little box or bag we keep our stash, tobacco and papers in. For me it was always about the fact that the box was visible to guests who came to my home; but unless I wanted them to know, it was my secret as to what it contained. Also, I'd had the thing for years. It was really hard for me to throw it out, but that made it all the more important for me to do so.

But it's actually quite valuable/It was given to me by my ex-partner/I brought it back from Mexico/India myself
For goodness sake, chuck it out! Is it really more valuable than your health, your future and your freedom?

Okay, when you're ready I suggest you put all your smoking paraphernalia into a cheap plastic supermarket bag and then go for a little walk before you go to bed. Find a public rubbish bin, tie a knot in the bag and drop it in. Remember to put something smokable into the bag, as well.

One Clearhead graduate put everything in a bag and gave it to her upstairs next-door-neighbour, who she used to share the occasional smoke with. A few days later, after she'd had a drink or two, she was knocking on her neighbour's door, begging for a smoke. She hadn't thrown her stuff far enough away, and subconsciously she knew it at the time.

I want to quit now but I've got a month's supply left and I don't feel ready to throw it all out. What should I do?

Well, since you ask, I suggest that you go ahead and chuck it all out anyway. I understand how hard it is. Many people have such a deep fear of running out of dope that the idea of not having any in your home, should the need become desperate, is terrifying. That may be why you tend to bulk buy in the first place.

The fact is that if you have it around or know where it is, chances are that you will succumb the first time you have really strong cravings. Why make it so easy to give in to your mind?

Be positive. Perhaps the process will be easier than you thought and you will be able to manage those first few days, weeks and months much more comfortably than you imagined. It's my experience that this is often the case. The braver you are now by removing temptation, the better your chances of success. It's not as if you can't replace it pretty much any time you want to, anyway.

I've done this so many times before. I threw everything out a long time ago

Okay, but chuck *something* out, even if it's only the last half of your last joint. Force yourself to give up something you'd rather not.

Less than your best

Do you have access to a camera? If you've allowed for yourself to get spectacularly mashed up tonight, why not take a little self-portrait of yourself looking less than your best? It's possible that you may look at this photograph with nostalgia in the future; on the other hand, in a few weeks' time, when people start to compliment you on how healthy you are looking, you may want to compare the photograph with what you see when you now look in the mirror. Seriously, either do it yourself or have someone do it for you. Notice how alive and alert you are looking. Are those red eyes due to the flash or the hash? Make a point of getting this picture printed, and put it alongside your motivation and visualization. Remember, your friends and family see you like this all of the time. They think this is your normal look. Could you prove them wrong?

You and your GP

Occasionally people contact us at Clearhead asking how cannabis is interacting with their anti-anxiety or anti-depression prescription, and what sort of effect stopping smoking will have on their medical symptoms. I don't think there is a simple answer to this question, because everybody has their own individual medical history with these conditions. The only sensible course of action is to talk with your GP and let him or her know about your concerns.

Not everybody has a good relationship with their doctor and dope smokers are no different. You may not fully trust him or her to treat these sensitive issues with confidentiality. But if you are considering completely stopping your cannabis use and are on psychiatric medication, this is too much of an important step to take without medical advice. If you have any doubts, or find that your GP is not taking the issue seriously or is being insensitive, it's very important to remain calm. Losing your temper or becoming emotional at this stage is not going to help the situation. But you do need to be firm and explain that cannabis has been an important part of your life for x number of years.

You also need to explain how often you use it and how you think it affects your existing depressive or anxiety symptoms. Your doctor should ask questions about your alcohol intake and other drug use at this stage; if they don't, tell them. Ideally, your doctor should agree to monitor you for three months after you stop smoking. He or she should agree to see you twice in the first six weeks, to check how you are doing and to see whether your prescription needs to be altered as the THC leaves your body.

If your GP offers to prescribe you anything from the benzodiazepine family of drugs, such as Valium or Diazepam, think very carefully about whether this is a path you want to go down. These are mood-altering drugs themselves, and also have the potential to become addictive in their own right. The fact is that although you may find it difficult to sleep for a short while after you quit smoking dope, taking prescribed tranquilizers will only prolong the problem. Tina, a lady who attended a recent workshop, was prescribed Valium by her GP but, after talking with her husband, decided not to take them. Within a few days her initial anxiety disappeared.

If you really don't want to have this conversation with your own practitioner, try and find someone neutral within the practice to explain your situation to. Perhaps the practice nurse would be a good person to approach first.

Confidentiality

As far as medical confidentiality is concerned, here in the UK this is an issue that more people are going to be thinking about over the next few years. At the time of writing (mid-2007), the National Health Service's new information technology system is being piloted and will be rolled out around the country as soon as all the bugs have been ironed out. Whilst in theory every adult consultation should be confidential, putting the nation's health records onto one enormous database leaves the information potentially vulnerable to hackers, although the Government claim that the system will in fact be *more* secure, as currently information is held on a non-secure paper and microfilm system. Presently, it is planned that patients will be given the opportunity to opt out of the system, although many GPs would actually like this changed to enable people to choose to opt in, rather than the other way round.

Your last smoke checklist

Chuck out every last bit of dope-smoking paraphernalia – find a bin away from your house and chuck it all out.

Make sure you chuck away at least some weed, grass or hash.

Take a photograph of yourself stoned, so you can remind yourself how awake and alert dope makes you look and feel when you've been caning it.

Visit your GP if you are prescribed drugs for anxiety or depression.

Section 4 Adjustment

19. Twenty-Four Hours

'All beginnings are somewhat strange; but we must have patience, and little by little, we shall find things that at first were obscure, becoming clearer.'

Vincent de Paul, 17th century saint, French

The first few days without weed are all about breaking the habit. At this stage you've still got plenty of THC in your system; in fact, if you were to be drug tested for cannabis at any time over the next four to six weeks, you would test positive. So on this, your first day of not smoking dope, it's not so much physical withdrawal you have to worry about, it's your mental attitude that will see you through.

There is really only one thing that you have to focus on today, and that's *not smoking dope*. Whether you have a busy day planned or you are already starting to worry about how you are going to fill your time, keep things simple. All you need to do to make today work for you is keep hold of the commitment you have made to positive change. Sounds simple, doesn't it? And by keeping a positive attitude, it really is.

A few years ago my niece emigrated to live in Melbourne, Australia – about as far as you can get from Europe, and a 24-

hour flight from London. My sister and her husband make the trip to see them as often as they can. They try to visit at the early part of the year, during our European winter, so as to get the benefit of some pleasant Australian summer sunshine during their stay. My sister is a very positive person; she was preparing to leave to visit my niece recently and was talking about the trip with a friend who told her that she was put off visiting Australia because of the "terrible" flight. "Of course," she said, "I know how much it means for you to see Karen, but I would struggle with such a long flight, even if it was my own kids out there. I hate flying anyway, and the idea of travelling such a long way over 24 hours would be incredibly stressful for me. I'd have to knock myself out with pills to even consider such a trip."

My sister has a completely different attitude. As far as she is concerned, being able to fly to Australia by taking just 24 hours out of her life is amazing. She considers the fact that she can board a plane on a cold, miserable January day in London and 24 hours later find herself on the other side of the world in sunny Melbourne totally magical.

A similar sort of positive mental attitude from you will help make this adjustment period much easier than if you make the mistake of slipping into a false belief that every day without smoking dope is going to be painful and difficult. Certainly some days over the next few weeks are bound to be challenging, but the personal strength and satisfaction you will gain from getting through awkward situations without reverting back to your cannabis crutch will be some of the most fulfilling of your life.

When was the last time you went fully 24 hours without cannabis? Unless you made a fairly recent attempt at quitting, without the support of this book, I'm guessing quite a long time ago. If you have followed the monitoring exercise in the last section, by now you should be used to not giving in to your mind every time it tells you that it's time to get stoned; but it is incessant, isn't it? Every few minutes your mind tells you that it's time for your THC fix, and every few minutes you wearily have to remind yourself that you don't smoke anymore.

I want you to add something to this little routine. Next time your mind says "Surely it's time to get stoned", take your right hand, place it on the opposite shoulder and tap yourself once or twice on your back. As you do so, say your own name and congratulate yourself. Acknowledge yourself for this step you are taking by literally patting yourself on the back. Now, this is the moment to remind yourself about the benefits you are looking to achieve from this process, and how every minute and every hour you go without smoking is a step closer to achieving your goals.

If you have been smoking every day for an extended period of time, cravings are going to be a natural part of the process but they only last as long as you allow them to hang around in your mind. Many people, whilst still actively addicted, have had the experience of traveling and being unable to get hold of a dope connection. They often tell me that while away they experienced only minor withdrawal, yet at different times when they consciously attempted to quit in their home environment, they found it much more difficult, and can't work out why.

Perhaps part of the answer is that when we are away from home we tend to be relaxed, as we take a break from our everyday routine, as well as being stimulated by our new surroundings. When people quit with us at Clearhead, it seems to be those that allow themselves to be most relaxed about the process who find the whole thing easiest, especially if they can keep themselves busy with new activities at the same time.

I'm sure there will be moments when it will feel like you are expending a lot of emotional energy simply by just not smoking. This sometimes amounts to a feeling of being overwhelmed by even the simplest interactions with other people, or becoming frustrated by what you would normally consider straightforward tasks. When you notice you are feeling this way, allow yourself to consciously relax by breathing slowly and steadily through your nose and with your mouth shut, for a few moments. Perhaps you might want to blow your nose first to make sure your nasal passages are clear. Try and breathe deeply, from your stomach rather than from higher up in your chest. You can place your hand over your tummy for a moment or two, checking that it is expanding and contracting as you breathe. Just for a short while, completely focus on breathing in this way. This is a proven method of calming yourself.

As you allow your breath to flow easily through your body, consciously remove whatever was bothering you from your mind. As you disassociate yourself from the problem even just for a minute or two, you will find that when you return to it you have gained some much-needed perspective and will be able to say what needs to be said calmly, or deal with the situation appropriately.

If you're working, it's more important during the day to keep yourself busy and briefly practise this controlled breathing only when you really need to, rather than unnecessarily breaking the rhythm of your day.

Not working?
If you're not at work today you may have more opportunity to practise longer relaxed breathing sessions, sitting or lying down for maybe 10 or 20 minutes. Perhaps you've been close to your home environment all day. If so, it's likely you will have been feeling quite restless, unable to focus on much other than getting through the day and not smoking.

Be easy on yourself. The smallest things that you are able to accomplish at this time are big achievements. Your mind may not be used to acknowledging them as such but, speaking from personal experience, I can promise you they are. If you haven't done so already, make a list of some things that you would like to do this week. These may be simple tasks that you have been putting off for some time, or possibly a new project that you have been waiting for an opportunity to get stuck in to for a while now. Start thinking about getting out of the house for a morning or an afternoon as a priority this week.

If you find the whole business of interacting with the outside world quite challenging, then set yourself short tasks to accomplish away from your home. This could mean simply taking the first steps toward finding some new resources to help with your anxiety, perhaps in the library, or making a point of going out to use the Internet.

If this sort of thing isn't a problem, start thinking in terms of *adventure*, visiting people you haven't seen for a while and who live in another area, or finding some small reason to make trips further afield. Don't be scared to call somebody positive in your life for support at this time. If they don't know about Operation Clearhead, you don't have to tell them immediately. It might be enough to call them for a chat. Listen to their stuff for a while, then, if it feels right, casually mention what's going on for you today.

Being a parent at home

If you are a parent of a young child or children, today will be like every other day – busy and possibly quite stressful, especially if you don't currently have a partner to share the responsibility. Perhaps you smoke to reward yourself at different times during the day – when your child or children are at school, for example. Now is the time to be positive. Spend some time figuring out how you can work at improving your parent–child communications in small ways. It's important to get off on the right foot, and loving gestures will make all the difference to how you feel about yourself and your family relationships at this time. As your mind clears today, allow yourself a few minutes to have some compassionate thoughts and feelings for yourself.

You have an incredibly tough job with awesome responsibilities, and all you can do is your best. Whilst we are smoking dope every day it's very easy to get caught up in negative thought patterns, judging ourselves as bad parents because of our lack of control with regard to our smoking. By facing up to and taking control of your cannabis habit, you are starting the process of ensuring that you will be physically and emotionally healthy as the years go by and your children grow up. For the moment, simply remind yourself of some of the benefits you will gain by loosening the control that dope holds over you, such as the extra time, energy and consistency that will undoubtedly enhance your parenting skills.

Coming home from work

If you've been at work all day then perhaps you will have found everything fairly straightforward so far, especially if smoking in the morning wasn't part of your routine. Like many dope smokers, you probably spend quite a lot of your working day wishing the hours away until you can get home and sink into your first joint of the evening. This in itself can be an insidious trap that slowly begins to remove small satisfactions from your working life, to the point where the only real satisfaction you are able to focus on is coming home to get stoned.

As the time gets closer to when you would normally find yourself rushing back for your nightly smoking session, you may start to feel uncomfortable or slightly panicky at the thought of returning to a weed-free environment. You can change this negativity around by reminding yourself of the reality of so many nights spent stoned at home, devoid of new social interaction. Often this scenario is a really strong motivation for you to make these positive changes in regard to your cannabis smoking. Certainly it was for me. I simply became bored with the narrowness of my existence. Sometimes it seemed that I had pared things down to a very basic lifestyle – work, eat, sleep, smoke and worry. Fun and spontaneity had become alien concepts to me. They only seemed to be part of the lives of other people, other couples.

Alternative activities

If your life has hit a similar point, where essentially it has been reduced to Home=stoned/work=thinking about being stoned, if you haven't already done so, you need to start **ACTIVELY** figuring out alternative ways to keep yourself entertained, without cannabis.

In case you missed it, the important word in the last sentence was **ACTIVELY.**

Daydreaming about improving ourselves and our situation is, curiously, easy to do when we spend a great deal of time stoned. Fantasizing about making new friends, enrolling in an interesting class, taking up old hobbies, or even becoming productive around the house is often no more than a fanciful wish list for the professional stoner. It's not that we don't want to make the effort, it's just that new things, people and experiences can take more energy and focused concentration than we can easily muster whilst we have a joint in our hand.

When I think about finding alternative activities I'm always reminded of the movie cop cliché where the detective says something like, "Look, you can do this the easy way or the hard way." And the same is true for you. I am not suggesting that you turn your life upside down and become a different person, but if you have been spending a lot of time at home over the years doing essentially passive activities whilst stoned, my guess is that if you take away ingredient X and still carry on with the same domestic routines, you will find the process of cannabis withdrawal much harder than if you had started to put a few alternative activities into place.

Perhaps this isn't you. A significant number of people have problems with their addictive relationship with cannabis whilst still remaining busy, combining work with active social lives, even fitness routines, and a generally productive lifestyle. I would still suggest that it will serve you well to shake things up a bit. It's not only being active that is important at this time, this is also about challenging yourself and your perceptions, to distract you as your mind and body adjust to their new freedom.

So, for example, if you keep yourself fit through swimming, try jogging; or visa versa. If you have a hectic lifestyle with seemingly no space for new activities, drop something, or somebody, and put one or two new hobbies, or people, into place. It's important to remember that experimenting with new pursuits doesn't mean you are committed to them forever. This is simply a strategy to keep your mind positively engaged at this time.

Incredible as it may seem right now, everybody who has been through this adjustment process finds that, if able to keep going, after a relatively short time you will find yourself going whole days at a time during which you don't think about dope once, as opposed to thinking about smoking a joint every few minutes. But it's much easier to reach this point if you are able to consistently distract yourself.

When I quit I gained physical and emotional energy that was difficult to come to terms with. Previously, every time I had attempted to stop I found simply being at home without weed extremely challenging. Sitting around doing very little except thinking how easy it would be to call my dealer was never going to be an effective strategy for me. So when I quit for the last, and final, time I did something that was uncharacteristic for me. I started to plan how I was going to manage my time. I chose five different things that I knew would support my decision to no longer smoke.

I started preparing more meals from scratch. I bought a bicycle and began riding it no matter what the weather. I stepped up my yoga, and started meditating for 10 minutes every morning before I left for work. I also started attending a 12-step programme, twice a week, which was incredibly supportive. Making the commitment to attend added real shape to my week, and even though I couldn't totally identify with everything said at the meetings, I took strength from being in the company of others who were struggling with their own problems in their own lives. If nothing else, this took the focus away from myself for a while.

Finally, be aware that physical activity of any type is invaluable to you at this time. If you are worried that you won't be able to sleep, or that you may become depressed without your nightly THC medication, physical exercise will tire you out as well as raise the feel-good chemicals in your brain. Dope smokers live in their heads. When we quit, we need to rediscover that we also inhabit bodies.

Clearhead's A–Z of alternative activities

Join a drama group and start Acting, or get some Acupuncture, help Amnesty International. Study Beauty therapy, brush up your Baking, buy a Bike, join a Book club. Express yourself through Creative writing, learn how to Co-Counsel. Start Decorating your home, join a Dance class, learn to Drive, accept Doubt. Clean up your local Environment, become Emotionally literate. Expect more from life. Prepare your Food with love, get down to the city Farm, study Film, stop Fantasizing. If it's summer, take up Gardening; if it's winter, join a Gym. Adopt a Greyhound. Study Herbalism, accept you're Human, get out of the House, learn Humility. Play a musical Instrument, study Interior design, do the Ironing, stay In touch. Join a Jazz club, start a Jewellery course, do a Juice detox, look for a new Job. Take up Knitting if you're a man, or Kickboxing if you're a woman. Join a Laughter club, study Life drawing, become a weekend Line dancer. Study Massage therapy, take up a Martial art, get into Meditation. Get to know your Neighbour, study Natural history, stop being Numb. Start painting with Oils, help out in the local Oxfam shop, become Optimistic. Teach yourself Photography, get Political, become a Potter (not pothead). Stop Questioning life, start living it – Start Questioning life, become curious. Take Riding lessons, start a Religion, help others learn to Read, start to Relax. Get down to the Swimming pool, or start Singing classes, learn to Sail. Stay Sober. Learn about your addictive behaviour, join a Twelve-step programme, Touch-Type. Join an Underwater diving club, discover that the Ultimate high can't be ingested. Help others by Volunteering, use the power of your Voice. Learn how to Work with Wood, build a Website or paint with Watercolours. Scare yourself silly, take up an Xtreme sport. Join a Yoga class, learn the secret of being forever Young. Study Zen by watching the animals at the Zoo.

Whatever you do, or don't do, resist the temptation to smoke. After a while you will think about it less and less, until one day you won't think about it at all.

Energy exchange

As it nears that time in the evening when we start to think that bed might be a sensible option, you may well find yourself actually feeling quite tired. This may come as a surprise to you if you have been concerned that the opposite would be the case. Broadly, people experience two different energy states as the THC begins to leave the body. Some people find their metabolism begins to speed up; they find their appetite diminishes and that consistent sleep is hard to come by. For others the reverse is true; they are tempted to eat more than usual and have low energy, feeling sluggish and tired. At different times during this adjustment period you may well find your energy changing from one state to the other. This should be expected, even though often you just wish things would even out and you were feeling 'normal' again.

What your body is doing at this time is slowly beginning to remember what normal actually felt like before you started smoking cannabis every day. If you have been smoking dope habitually and heavily for any length of time, how could it be any other way?

Cannabis users have a perception that the habit is essentially benign. We think of herbal cannabis as a natural substance and compare its effects positively with alcohol, heroin, cocaine and tobacco. We don't think in terms of physical withdrawal, but it is, I'm afraid, completely unrealistic to suppose that there has been no physiological effect on our bodies over the years. The average length of time most people who join the Clearhead weekend have been smoking for is 17 years, or on an everyday basis 14 years. This is a long stretch of time by any reckoning. Within that range there are some who have been smoking daily for 30 years plus, whilst others might have been smoking every day for five years. Even five years is a significant amount of time to be daily ingesting any sort of drug or herbal remedy, whether cannabis or anything else.

Sleeping

As you can imagine, I've spent a fair amount of time whilst researching this book reading material and talking to the medical profession about cannabis addiction, and I do get frustrated when I read or hear 'expert' opinion dismissing the sleep disruption cannabis withdrawal can cause as inconsequential. I know from my own experience and from working with so many others how this particular issue can often be the one thing that keeps us stuck, when everything else in our lives points toward quitting.

Conversely I have also met a surprising number of habitual smokers who tell me that their heavy cannabis use has the effect of stimulating them at night so they can't sleep when stoned. But by far the largest proportion of dope smokers either consciously or unconsciously have fallen into the habit of using cannabis as a sleeping aid.

This can be a problem for a variety of reasons. Many people who smoke dope heavily before bed struggle to get up in the morning and feel that their brains don't start working effectively until they've had their first joint of the day. I am also of the opinion that when you go to bed stoned the quality of your sleep is severely reduced. When I was smoking I always used to wake up feeling drained and tired.

Today just the opposite is true. I awake feeling refreshed and re-energized, fully alert as I open my eyes in the morning.

The important thing to remember is that, like every other aspect of this adjustment period, for most people disrupted sleep only lasts a relatively short while.

When Linda attended her Clearhead workshop, all she would talk about throughout the weekend were her concerns about sleep. She told us that quite often if she didn't feel stoned enough before bed she would phone or visit friends at ridiculous hours to get hold of one or two more spliffs to knock herself out. Of all the participants at Clearhead, nobody had more fear about not being able to sleep than Linda.

But Linda knew she had to quit. Smoking dope was ruining her relationship with her boyfriend, as well as causing her to make more and more stupid mistakes at work. As she told us, "Weed is turning my brain to mush." I received a wonderful email from Linda two months after the weekend, telling me that her sleep pattern had now returned to normal, and how grateful she was to find that she could get a satisfying night's sleep without drugs or alcohol. Her message to you, the reader, is simply that before she attempted to quit she would never have believed that such a change would be possible.

I'm afraid there is nothing I can do personally to solve the sleep issue for you, except by not pretending that it doesn't exist, and by repeating: **It is worth this temporary disruption to change your life and get beyond the cannabis addiction that is controlling you.** I would also like to remind you that, increasingly, sleep issues are affecting more and more of the general population, as we struggle to deal with our stressful lifestyles, and consequently there are plenty of books and websites, some of which are listed in the resource section, which offer the best possible advice as to how to minimize the symptoms.

I will pass on one general piece of advice from my own experience, that worked for me with this problem, and that was to not let my mind spiral into frustration and negativity. Sometimes when unable to sleep, especially if I knew I had an important day ahead at work, I used to build myself into a terrible state of frustration. As the hours ticked by I would become more and more angry at the thought of another hour lost lying awake when I *should* have been fast asleep. Of course, the more angry and frustrated I allowed myself to become, the less the likelihood of getting any sleep.

Eventually I figured out that it was more sensible to consciously relax about the whole thing and to fully value the few hours of sleep that I did attain, rather than fill myself with resentment over the hours that I had missed. I found it soothing to remind myself that although I wasn't actually asleep, I was resting. I had spent all day yesterday living my busy life and I would do the same thing again tomorrow, but right now belonged to me. Not surprisingly, as soon as I began to take the pressure off myself I would begin to relax and sleep would come.

Good sleep habit checklist
- Make it an evening habit to write a list of all that needs to be done over the next few days. This may help you let go of them, rather than lie awake worrying.

- Before you let yourself drift off, consider two or three things that you are grateful for in your life – a good friend, some skill or ability you have, for example.

- Try and avoid caffeine after midday. Replace with camomile tea before bed. It works!

- Replacing cannabis with alcohol on a regular basis to knock you out is not going to change anything except replace one problem with another. The quality of your sleep is likely to be even worse than when you were still smoking dope.

- Likewise, prescribed sleeping pills should only be used as a last resort, and then the smallest possible dosage.

- Some people find using herbal remedies such as Nightol

or Kalms, or products containing Valerian, works for them; others complain that they either don't work or leave them feeling drowsy, whilst still unable to sleep.

- Get some physical exercise during the day.

- Try to avoid eating a heavy meal before bed – have a light supper. If you are still hungry just before bed, have a further snack, maybe a piece of fruit, one small bowl of cereal, or some crackers.

- A warm bath is a great way to relax the body before bed, although don't overdo it – too long or too hot can stimulate you.

- Take advantage of all the hand-made and organic herbal products available for this problem. Whether for the bath or under the pillow, they will all help.

- Make sure your bedding and nightclothes are kept fresh and changed regularly.

- Try and keep your bedroom for sleeping; try not to watch television in bed before sleep – you'll only wake up with some very strange dreams. Replace with an audio book. Invest in a CD player or download device with head-phones.

20. Seven Days

'The best thing (and the worst thing) about getting clean was discovering I had feelings again.'
Well-known recovery observation

As I write this section of the book I'm intensely aware of how important it is to balance an explanation of the reality of cannabis withdrawal with not wanting to put the reader off from experiencing it themselves. For some people the whole process can be remarkably straightforward, which may explain the myth that quitting cannabis is a walk in the park. For others, however, there is a period of significant physical and emotional adjustment.

Whilst I was still smoking and trying to quit over a long time, one of the things that made my attempts harder and more demoralizing than they might have been was the almost universal dismissal from the medical and drug treatment professions about the reality of cannabis withdrawal. The process seemed to be classified as something so insignificant as to not be worth analysing or understanding.

As soon as I appreciated that there were others who were suffering the same symptoms, the same frustrations, I found the process not only possible but also, in a strange way, enjoyable. It was such a relief to realize that I wasn't alone, that I wasn't a failure because my attempts to quit using a drug that was supposedly non-addictive kept on ending in feelings of inadequacy and frustration.

As long as I was able to dig deep and remember my personal motivation for quitting, and the things that I wanted from my life that were missing because of my cannabis dependency, the reality, however tough, would undoubtedly be worth it. What I did not expect, especially during the early days of the process, was quite how much better I would feel when I pushed through to the other side and was finally free of a dependency that I thought would be with me for life.

As I began working with others, firstly on the UK Marijuana Anonymous helpline and then with Clearhead, I could see patterns emerging, defined stages and timelines that, although different for individuals, could be used to offer encouragement when most needed.

One day at a time

Perhaps one of the most well-known sayings from the 12-step programme is also one of the most simple – 'Take your sobriety one day at a time'. And this is what you must do. Every 24 hours that pass without giving in to your cravings for cannabis is an achievement, and should be acknowledged by yourself as such. When I quit I would often review the day, counting my blessings for what was good in my life; and I would always end on the fact that I had gone one more day without smoking, which I reminded myself was the biggest blessing of all.

After I had made it past day three, whilst still keeping 'one day at a time' in mind I was determined to last a week. If you have managed to go seven days without smoking, well done, you have completed a stage that in many ways is the hardest. Best of all, you have momentum.

Some common symptoms

The following are some of the most common symptoms that people experience when they quit smoking dope. Cannabis withdrawal affects different people in a variety of different ways. You may experience some of these symptoms, possibly all of them, or maybe none, but..

Please don't make the mistake of letting your imagination create those that aren't there.

My time estimates are approximate, so prepare for some variation, but don't expect the worst and you may be pleasantly surprised.

If you are a nicotine addict and still smoking cigarettes, you will almost certainly have found your consumption rocketing

"Every cigarette I smoke tastes disgusting; each time I light up I wish it was a joint. I'm only taking a drag or two before stubbing it out." If this is you then you have my sympathy. Nobody wants to quit dope and replace it with tobacco, but if you have been smoking tobacco joints and have decided that it would be too hard to quit both together, then this is probably your reality for the moment. So many people try and quit nicotine and cannabis at the same time, only to find they have taken on more than they can handle and end up back exactly where they started.

If you feel comfortable with nicotine replacement therapy (NRT) then you should definitely consider limited use of patches and/or an inhaler to take the edge off your craving. The initial urge to chain smoke will diminish over the next three to four weeks. My advice is not to quit cigarettes earlier than you originally planned. I suggest you need to think in terms of a year before attempting to quit tobacco. By then, if you've managed to quit weed, you will have the confidence and willpower to take advantage of the mainstream support there is out there to help you become the clean-lunged *total* non-smoker that you've aspired to be all of those years. If you feel resolute enough to stop smoking sooner, do so; but if you haven't planned to do so at the beginning, it's a mistake to **suddenly** quit tobacco at least within the first three months of adjusting to life without cannabis.

If you have been suffering from night and day sweats, you may not believe that simply smoking dope could cause such an obvious symptom of detoxification.

Most detoxification involves some sweating and should be encouraged by drinking much more water than usual – try for at least 2 litres per day. THC will be expelled through your urine and your sweat quite naturally, but hot baths, plenty of exercise as well as sauna or steam treatments will speed the process.

You should make the effort to visit your local pool or leisure centre as much as possible over the first month of detox. If you can afford to treat yourself to at least one massage a week, or maybe some reflexology or acupuncture, you should do this. Don't be afraid to invest in **yourself** at this time, using some of the money you are not spending on weed every week.

Night sweats are difficult because, combined with light sleeping, they can cause discomfort to your partner as well as yourself. If this is a problem, consider sleeping separately for a short while. It's definitely worth making sure you have enough clean bedding to change in the night, as well as a clean set of clothes to change into if you find yourself sweating during the day. There is no point in being slack about staying fresh; the more comfortable you are, the better you will feel about yourself and what you are doing. The sweating can last for anything up to 21 days, but usually you are over the worst after about 10.

If you experience an episode of hand or body shakes and tremors

A few people experience episodes of shaking and tremors, which can come as a shock if you thought this was something strictly related to alcohol or heroin withdrawal. This symptom is almost always a one- or two-time deal. If you are in the privacy of your own home, my advice would be to go for it, by exaggerating the action until your hand, or whichever part of your body is shaking, is exhausted, which should take about 10 minutes.

If you feel you want to experience a whole body shake, take a grounded standing position with your legs a few feet apart, bend your knees slightly, and start to shake your body from your upper legs. After a while, if it feels right, move to some comfortable cushions or pillows placed on the floor and continue, allowing yourself to jerk quite strenuously until you have nothing left to shake. Afterward, don't do anything other than rest, for at least half an hour. If at any time during this exercise you feel a strain to any part of your body, stop right away, which you can easily do by taking some deep breaths to slow your self down.

If you have found it difficult to eat normally, through loss of appetite, you may be feeling weak and slightly sick

Some people experience stomach cramps during cannabis withdrawal. If you have been having these since before quitting but they are worsening, you need to get to your doctor to make sure there isn't an underlying condition. If they have just started since you quit, this is of course debilitating but not too serious. I recommend plenty of ginger or peppermint tea throughout the course of the day, and stick to bland food until you start to feel better. Usually stomach ache only lasts a day or two at most. If it continues for much longer then, again, make an appointment with the doctor.

If you are experiencing a loss of appetite, be reassured that this is a very common symptom. The important thing is to make sure you are taking some nutrients onboard, otherwise you will start to feel weak, light-headed and slightly sick.

Go to the pharmacy and pick up the best multi-vitamins

they have. Take them every day for the next two months. If you have a blender in the kitchen, start making fruit smoothies for yourself. Make sure you have at least a glass or more for breakfast, and try and have a couple of bananas or some dried fruit and nuts as snacks during the day. Ideally, have a full bowl of light soup for both lunch and dinner. Try and eat the soup with some bread or crackers if you can. It's important to make the effort.

Your appetite will come back, quite naturally, in about five or six days. The trick is to notice it when it does and then act upon it.

If you are feeling constantly tired and lethargic you may be thinking that you will never regain your energy

Your energy will return, I assure you. You may be feeling this way because your dope smoking has been masking an unhealthy lifestyle that doesn't include enough sleep, but more likely your metabolism is slowing down whilst your body gets used to its new condition. This can feel like jet lag, and the best advice is to treat it as such; in other words, try not to go to bed as soon as you come home from work, otherwise you may well get locked in a cycle of waking up in the early hours, having slept through the evening. It's much better to hang on for as long as possible before going to bed.

I appreciate that many of the ideas and plans you might have had for alternative activities may feel beyond you right now, but that's no reason to give up on them. Do what you can, even if that just involves going out to the movies rather than watching TV at home. Continue to put plans in place for more adventurous activities when your energy has returned to normal, which will be in approximately three or four weeks' time.

If it feels like you haven't slept properly for ages, you may be wondering when you will next enjoy deep sleep
As discussed in the previous chapter, this can be the hardest obstacle for some people, especially if you lead a stressful life and have been using weed to keep you going for years. Remember, acceptance and preparation are the keys to easing the process. Most people find the first three or four nights the hardest, perhaps only grabbing a few hours of disturbed sleep, but usually by the fifth night nature takes its course and you get a decent amount of sleep. Slowly, slowly, the balance begins to return to normal. If you follow at least some of the suggestions in the previous chapter you will make the process easier.

I have spoken to some people who after six months say they are still not sleeping well. This is almost always connected to not understanding how to relax naturally. The obvious way to work through this is to regularly put yourself in a state somewhere between sleep and wakefulness, perhaps by using a favourite hypnotherapy recording, maybe med-itation, or simply lying down on the floor listening to a much-loved piece of music for half an hour will do the trick. Don't make yourself too comfortable, train yourself not to fall asleep whilst you are in this naturally tranquil state. Finding time for natural relaxation will refresh you, and retune your body and mind to appreciate the difference between the sleep and waking states.

If you are having vivid dreams, or even nightmares, you may be concerned that your dreams will always be this intense

If you have been smoking weed for a few years and it is your habit to smoke before bed, it is unlikely you will have been aware of your dream life.

Cannabis severely reduces the time between the initiation of your dream and when it is detectable in stage 3 sleep, as well as often eliminating dreaming completely when you reach stage 4 sleep (REM stage).

Interestingly, REM (Rapid Eye Movement) stage sleep is also vital for the consolidation of short-term memory into long-term memory.

To explain further, sleep is divided into four stages.

Stage 1 – A very light stage of sleep lasting only a few minutes.

Stage 2 – The dreaming process begins with vague thoughts and unclear images.

Stage 3 – Body functions slow down. It's hard to wake someone during this stage.

Stage 4 – REM. This is where most dreams occur.

So if you are starting to experience your dream life again, its intensity will probably come as a shock. Intense dreams can be draining in their own right. But dreaming is fundamentally healthy, and, like everything else in this process, the intensity of the experience will calm down with time. If you're suffering nightmares, and plenty of people do, usually their frequency will decrease after between two and three weeks, to be gradually replaced by more benign dream experiences. You will begin to get used to a normal dream life again over a slightly longer period of up to six weeks.

Most people find experiencing their dreams again an unexpected bonus. It can be fascinating to have a pad by your bed to make a note of what's going on, and then to check to see what makes sense when you re-visit them the next day.

If you are suffering extra anxiety, you may not understand why, nor what you can do about it

A percentage of people who quit smoking cannabis find they become overly anxious throughout the withdrawal process. I will always remember one Clearhead attendee who when asked on the pre-course questionnaire whether she suffered panic attacks replied honestly, 'The only time I have ever experienced a panic attack is when I think about quitting.' Sure enough, soon after she quit she suffered two panic attacks when she thought she was going to be late for appointments.

Anxiety or panic attacks, whether brought on by smoking cannabis or when attempting to quit, can be symptomatic of deeper emotional problems, which need to be worked through with counselling or therapy (see recovery section). Nevertheless, at the moment you are experiencing them the sense of fear can be both irrational and overwhelming. I strongly recommend that you don't go down the route of looking for a prescribed medical solution. A period of with-drawal-induced anxiety is usually a relatively short-term phenomenon, and there are plenty of natural therapies available to ease you through. If you are unlucky enough to be feeling more than usually anxious, treat this as an opport-unity to analyse what might be causing these stress episodes.

Does it feel as though there is a lack of control somewhere in your life? Are you a perfectionist finding your role too hard to keep together now you are not smoking? Are you anxious about death, commitment, or poverty? You now have a window of opportunity to examine what is going on inside your head that is causing your irrational fear. Like the other symptoms the anxiety feelings will gradually calm down over the next few weeks.

Often we feel panicky when we wake worried about the day ahead. Morning meditation can work wonders to help settle your nerves, and prepare you for the day. Or you, you may be surprised at how a cold shower will change your mood, give you courage and refresh you.

If you find yourself emotionally overwhelmed and close to tears much of the time, you may be wondering if it is safe to let go and release your feelings
Crying is as natural as it is healthy; and yes, for both men and women. Some people keep *untold* sadness at bay by spending their lives stoned, or drunk, or whatever else they might use to keep painful memories under lock and key.

Sometimes this is a conscious decision, but so often we don't realize why we do what we do. Because many drug treatment authorities don't put cannabis dependency in the same class as alcohol or heroin addiction, dope smokers themselves are often surprised at how much emotional intensity they have been bottling up over the years. When we quit smoking dope, very often we need to cry but we are scared of feeling overwhelmed in an inappropriate situation – at work, for example. If it does all feel too much at the wrong time, this is a definite signal that you need to shed some tears in a safe place.

Many of us, especially men, find it almost impossible to cry. Either we were taught by others not to, or we trained ourselves to not show any external vulnerability. Without our cannabis crutch, and yet unable to shed tears, can lead to a distinctly uncomfortable feeling of fragility. This is when we need to find some privacy and consciously look for tear triggers. Sad films, emotional music, for example; maybe rediscovering some deeply meaningful photographs or letters can do the trick.

Another thing that can hold us back from this natural release is a feeling that we have so many tears to shed that once we start we will never stop. Try and remember just how early you are in the process. Don't force anything. You may have been living in a numb, anesthetized state for a number of years, possibly without even realizing it.

For me personally, I found the answer was to join a laughter club. Laughter is the other side of sadness, and I discovered I could shed tears of laughter much more easily than those of sadness, anger or frustration. The laughter network is a brilliant international organization dedicated to helping people start to feel again through simply triggering their laughter reflex. (See resource section).

A whole piece on anger

Anger is as legitimate as any other emotion. Whilst I was smoking I never thought of myself as angry, because for so many years I was especially careful to quickly suppress any anger I felt by smoking another joint; although one way or another my feelings used to leak out, in resentment, judgement and irritability.

Strong new angry feelings emerge in so many people who go through cannabis withdrawal, so when you are feeling at your most confrontational, try and remember this is about the process as much as it is about you. The anger we feel at this time is often irrational and out of proportion to the situation. When we feel rage like this we are tapping directly into all our deepest frustrations, what the philosopher Ekhart Tolle calls the 'Pain Body'; a part of us that holds every slight, every unfairness, every ounce of self-pity, defensiveness and self-righteousness.

Many of us were brought up in families in which it was not okay to express anger; others have grown up with the anger of parents or siblings, and will have found their own ways to cope with this. It may not be generally accepted, but in my opinion cannabis tends to attract people who are either angry or are uncomfortable with anger.

None of this helps us when we have just *lost it* and we wish we could take back our outburst. Well, here is some practical advice. You can take it back. If you've really lost your temper at this time, whether you felt justified or not, be quick to apologize. Your justification might be totally appropriate but your reaction surely isn't. This is really important, because the most crucial lesson you will learn as a recovering addict is what a relief it is to let go of our ego. There will probably be resistance from the part of you that is never wrong, but override it and allow some humility into your life. Sometimes in these first few weeks without dope we often find the need to express long pent-up anger with others and say things that have needed to be said for ages. The ancient Greek philosopher Aristotle put it best when he said: "Anyone can become angry. That is easy. But to be angry with the right person, to the right degree, at the right time, for the right purpose and in the right way - that is not easy."

Perhaps you might need to write a letter to someone rather that express your anger verbally. You might write this letter never meaning to send it. This can be a trial run, allowing you to think coolly about what you want to say before you articulate it verbally. You might simply want to scream and shout. This should be easier to do than it actually is. I would love to see anger clubs, where people could get together to learn how to rant and rage safely without judging themselves or each other. However, until such a facility is created, here are a few alternatives.

If you are a driver, being in a car parked alone in a quiet

place can provide the opportunity to have a good, loud scream.

In the privacy of your home, give a pillow or cushion some punishment.

Get up early, or late in the evening, find some countryside or a city park and let loose with a bellow or two.

Join a martial arts, boxing or wrestling club.

The good news is that these strong feeling of rage will tend to dissipate in their intensity over the next few weeks; in fact, unbelievable as it might sound to you right now, you will become noticeably calmer without cannabis as the following weeks turn into months. This is simply because as you become more aware of how you are feeling, it becomes easier to process your moods appropriately, without reacting immediately.

Lastly on the theme of anger although this is a rare occurrence I need to address physical violence. If you find yourself actually committing a physical act against somebody: this is a serious problem and you need to find help right now. **Apologizing is not going to be enough!**

Should you start smoking cannabis again? If you are express-ing violence, only you, and those close to you can make that decision, but in the long term pacifying your rage with dope is not a solution.

21. First Weekend

Sometimes in our working lives it feels a battle just to keep going until the end of the week. For so many of us, Friday night represents an opportunity to let off steam without having to pay the consequences at work the next morning. Many times people have told me, especially those quitting weed without any proper support, that their minds have tricked them at this stage. The most common deception is to start thinking that somehow you've proven that you can quit and so it's therefore okay to start smoking again. But what would be the point of that? You are, and would continue to be, just as trapped and addicted as if you had never stopped at all. We might like to pretend that the weekend is a magical couple of days on which you can have the odd smoke when it's around and still carry through your original plan of abstinence. I wish it were so, but it's not. I promise you nobody, and I mean nobody, can go from being a dependent weed smoker to a weekend recreational toker in just a few days or weeks. It doesn't work like that.

Perhaps we are fooled because we have friends who habitually binge on booze, weed and coke (and anything else they can get their hands on) every Friday and Saturday night, and still appear to be able to leave it all alone until the following weekend. Surely, we think, if they can handle their drugs it's okay for me to enjoy myself on the weekend, as well. The truth is that we are all different, and have different priorities at different times of our lives. Binging on potentially addictive substances is a dangerous game to play, and there will come a time in many people's lives when serious choices have to be made. Right now you have made a serious commitment to *yourself* and *your* circumstances and there is no point in drawing comparisons with others at this stage.

For example, I've known one or two people to turn up to their first week support group incredibly proud that they spent Friday night taking cocaine and drinking but didn't succumb to the joints being passed around. This is not going to work. Alcohol and other mood-altering drugs are highly addictive substances; substituting one addictive behaviour for others is a recognized and familiar syndrome, known as *cross-addiction*.

The 12-step fellowships are abstinence based. At meetings it is suggested that you do not use any mind-altering substances whilst you are following the programme. That means if you have a problem with alcohol – no weed or other drugs; if you are addicted to heroin or other hard drugs – one drink or joint could send you back to your primary drug of choice. It is true that *inebriation breeds inebriation*. For example, as a cannabis addict, if you drink to get drunk on a regular basis during the first few months of your new dope-free life, it will almost certainly trigger a desire to smoke a joint. You may be strong enough not to act on this desire in the short term, but if you consistently seek to chemically alter how you are feeling, you will either do a complete *cross-addiction* or you will eventually give in to your core urge to smoke dope; and before you know it you will be back where you started.

Realistically, not everybody is able to completely stop drinking, but at Clearhead we strongly advise you not to drink for the first three months, to give your mind and body a chance to really appreciate the benefits of sobriety.

If you think in terms of a healthy lifestyle, there are other, less destructive ways to alter your mood and have fun. If you do find yourself in a drinking situation, put a limit on your desire to get drunk. Drink slowly, allow yourself to enjoy a limited buzz whilst maintaining control of your faculties. You will thank yourself the next day.

Your first weekend without dope could be the opportunity to practise a different kind of relaxation. Peace of mind, for instance, is tremendously relaxing. It might sound like going from the sublime to the ridiculous, but tackling some of those personal and domestic issues (balancing your bank account, doing the ironing), that you have been avoiding will actually give you a real feeling of satisfaction once you make a start on them. Perhaps you could follow this up with a swim in the local pool, followed by a massage and a sauna session, for example. However you decide to spend your weekends, enjoying them in *real time* will make a pleasant change; and as you begin to accomplish more in your free time, you will appreciate the extra choices available to you when the basics are taken care of.

22. From Four to Eight to Twelve weeks

Mini-revolt

At Clearhead we have found that it takes, on average, around four to six weeks for most people to fully adjust to not using cannabis. As we have seen, some will adjust more quickly, whilst others will still hit upon lingering symptoms up to two months after smoking their last joint. For some reason, we have also found that the four-week mark is particularly difficult. Even people who have found the process relatively straightforward sometimes find that during their fourth week without weed a mental switch clicks, which triggers a mini-revolt as the addictive part of your mind finally realizes that you ain't going to go back to your old ways anytime soon. At this point it may seem, for a day or two, that you are back to square one; but it will pass quickly enough, providing you don't give in to temptation.

Feeling better

When we start to feel better, it doesn't all come at once. It's a subtle feeling of well-being, almost like the high we got when we started smoking dope in the early days. For me it was deeply connected with my personal confidence. I clearly remember, after having quit, meeting a neighbour in the street. We stopped to chat for a few minutes, and as we went our separate ways I realized that although he was someone who I had known by sight for years, I had never actually spoken more than a few words to him before. I thought about how nice it was to have eye contact with him, whereas before, when I was stoned, that wouldn't have been possible. I reflected that I didn't feel guilty as we spoke; I didn't feel that I was less than him in some way, which I suddenly realized was my default position in so many of my personal relationships. It wasn't that I wanted him as my new best friend, but the feeling of confidence gained from that small interaction really felt good.

The feeling of well-being grew inside as I realized that I hadn't gone this long without cannabis for years. I actually felt proud of myself as I considered it possible that this time I might finally be strong enough not to go back to smoking. My days were full of ups and downs, of course, but every time I dealt with a problem without calling my dealer I reinforced what for me was a brand new concept, that I didn't need weed to cope with the difficulties in my life.

Sometimes during this period we are tested and life lands us in an unexpectedly stressful situation. Coping without resorting to weed at this time won't be easy, but that's no reason to give up on yourself. *Accept the challenge!* Many people who have come through sudden developments or problems in their lives in their first few weeks of their new life tell me how pleased they were to have a straight head at this time otherwise they would never have been able to deal with what needed to be done.

Slowly, amongst the uncomfortable feelings that I was learning to get used to, I noticed a strange new sort of emotion I couldn't put my finger on, and if I tried to then often it would disappear. It was a sort of mixture of happiness, satisfaction, and contentment that later on in my recovery I recognized as joy. It came as a tremendous surprise to realize that amongst so many other negative feelings I had been numbing for such a long time were these more positive emotions. I remembered an occasion years ago that seemed idyllic, watching a sunset while on holiday with my then girlfriend, alone together in beautiful countryside. I distinctly remember telling myself that we had to smoke a joint for the moment to be perfect. Could it have been possible that I was actually scared to allow genuine, unfiltered joy into my life?

Regret and guilt

For many of us at this time, a shocking insight such as this can trigger terrible feelings of guilt and regret. These feelings can, at this point of the process, be incredibly intense, but I want to tell you now that they can also be dangerous, an active threat to your recovery and well-being. (These feelings are discussed in greater depth in the recovery section.)

Lapse and relapse

At this stage some of you may be thinking, *This is all very well, but supposing I haven't managed to completely stop smoking weed, what then? Have I failed?* This is tricky, but one thing I am absolutely clear about is **no, you haven't failed**. There is in fact no such thing as failure in recovery from addiction; it's a unique learning process like no other in life, and must be treated as such.

I think the best way for you to consider where you are with your personal relationship with weed is to offer some lapse and relapse scenarios to consider.

Take Joe, for example. After setting a date to quit on a Saturday night, he lasted until Monday evening, when he couldn't resist meeting up with a friend who laid some weed on him. Joe smoked every evening for the next week, until his new supply had run out. The following weekend he attempted to quit again, this time successfully. Looking back, he said that although his head had said goodbye to weed he needed to smoke for a short while longer so that finally he was able to feel it in his heart, as well.

Theresa was different; she went five days and nights without smoking. For her the experience was absolute hell. On Saturday night she asked her son to let her have a little something just so that she could get some sleep. She repeated the process on Sunday, and told herself that as long as she could just smoke before going to bed she would have regained control of her addiction. This lasted for about two weeks, but one day, after a particularly stressful day at work, she lit up as soon as she got home. Now she is back at the point at which she made the decision to quit in the first place, where every minute she is not working is spent stoned. She is slowly building up to the point where she will make another attempt at quitting.

Albie was determined to quit smoking weed this time. He had tried so many times before, each attempt ending in failure. After seven weeks he was starting to feel healthier than he had done for ages, but since even before he picked his quit date he knew that his friend's wedding was on the horizon. At the time of planning, he had been confident that he would be able to resist partaking in the numerous joints that his friends would be enjoying, but as the wedding drew closer the temptation began to prey on his mind, until three days before the big day he made the decision that he was going to use the occasion to get high.

Sure enough, he smoked, and really enjoyed himself, although he soon discovered that his tolerance for THC was so low that even half a joint had a big effect on him. As the evening progressed he shared at least five or six joints, and continued to feel good. The next day though, he felt terrible; his body ached simply from the effects of the weed, and his head was muddled. He wasn't tempted to carry on smoking that day. In fact, it took the best part of four days for his head to once again clear to the point it had been prior to the wedding. A few weeks later and there is another party coming up, at which he hasn't yet decided whether he will smoke again.

Never having attempted to quit before, Bill found the process much harder than he thought it would be, but after three weeks he felt the worst was over. After around two months the initial excitement of quitting, which had kept him going, had all but disappeared. Nothing much had changed in his life except he wasn't smoking anymore; all of his plans to try new things had slipped by the wayside. Although he was feeling sharper and healthier, he was also bored. One Friday night, almost without thinking about it, Bill found himself calling his dealer. Two hours later he was stoned, wondering what all the fuss was about. His body was sensitive to the weed, and to begin with it didn't take much to get him stoned.

On that Friday night Bill made a new deal with himself to only smoke on weekends. But when Monday rolled along he carried on smoking. The next new deal was only to smoke in the evenings; but by the end of the following week he was back toking before work again. In three weeks, precisely the length of time it took him to get through the worst of the withdrawal, he was back smoking, with all the same negative side-effects that had made him want to quit in the first place. It will take Bill a little while before he is ready to attempt to quit again, but I'm sure he will having learnt a valuable lesson.

Jack ran a successful business with his partners. He worked hard but his stress levels were very high. Before he quit, his addiction had been so full-on that he was smoking throughout the working day. His partners were less than impressed, and he was given a chance to clean up. Jack made excellent progress. He felt so much more confident, happy, and clearheaded and his wife was really happy with her *new* husband.

One day on his way home, on impulse he decided to visit a smoking buddy who he had avoided since quitting. Jack sat in his car outside his friend's house for ages, deciding whether to go in. Once the decision was made he had half a joint with his friend, which felt more than enough. At home, his wife noticed he was stoned immediately and wasn't pleased. Now three months after he first quit, Jack visits his friend every Friday night and they get stoned together like they used to. Jack is happy with this arrangement, but this Friday his mate gave him a bit of weed to take home for the weekend, and Jack is already thinking about how to steer clear of his wife for a few hours tomorrow.

Lastly, Carol quit 10 weeks ago; everything is going so well in her life. She finds her job so much easier now she isn't smoking every evening and weekend. She is also in a new relationship, for the first time ever with someone who doesn't smoke weed. She's not bored; in fact her life is really busy with all sorts of new people and activities. But for a while now she has had a nagging itch that she wants to scratch. She is deeply curious about getting stoned again. She thinks about it more and more often, and if the opportunity arose she is not sure if she could resist. Carol can hardly remember what it feels like to be stoned, and that bothers her. She is also curious to know if it really was such a problem. In the end, Carol decided not to smoke. She stopped obsessing about it and re-committed mentally to her original decision. The itch, like itches do when you don't scratch them, went away.

The most important thing to understand about lapsing or relapsing is that it does not signify failure. It's very easy to say to ourselves, "I tried to get clean but it didn't work", and then to give up on ourselves for another few months, or years, until we are ready to address the situation again. This is an unnecessary but common mistake, coming from our addictive mindset, which ignores the significant progress made, the lessons learnt, and the rewards of recovery. Don't let a lapse turn in to a relapse. (see chapter 29)

23. Okay, so I've Quit. What Now?

When we stop active addiction, even after a long period many people waste energy simply wishing that they could smoke again. Even those of us who have been taught by experience that one smoke eventually leads us back to where we started, are at some point likely to feel deprived by not being able to indulge in the occasional high.

So much has changed in our life. There are huge tangible benefits but there are also things we miss. Life can seem, perhaps more boring, drab, or grey. This is a state of mind, of course, but also completely understandable, and there is really only one way that I have found to square the circle.

I start by remembering how young I was when I first started smoking dope, and how quickly I became dependent on smoking every day. I reflect that even though I haven't smoked a joint in over five years, compared to my 30 years of hard smoking this is not a very long time. If you have only been clean five or six months, for example, and you smoked habitually for 10 years, perhaps we are in a similar place.

I then recall myself as a stoner – the good times, of course, but also the times when I used to smoke just because that's what I did, that's who I was. I remember how I smoked not because I enjoyed it much anymore but because weed had become so much a part of me that the idea of even a day without smoking was a terrifying prospect.

I then start to consider how I am now a different person to the younger me that was obsessed with, and then addicted to, smoking weed. Not necessarily a better person, but certainly older and wiser. This allows me to look forward, to consider my understandable desire to get high as belonging to a former life, the person I used to be, not the person I am now.

Sometimes, like every ex-cannibis smoker I have ever met, I will dream at night that I am still toking. Sometimes I will wake feeling disappointed that it was only a dream; more often I wake feeling relieved. All of this is a natural process leading toward recovery.

Section Five Recovery

24. What is Recovery?

Before I had to find out for myself, I never really understood what people meant when they talked about recovery from addiction. Recovery, of course, suggests illness, which fits with the view many addicts and drug professionals have with regard to addiction being a disease. Personally, I struggle with this concept, especially the extension that the disease of addiction is incurable. But whatever my own beliefs about addiction and recovery, I appreciate that the potential outcomes are too serious and personal for one person to disrespect the point of view of others.

However, I generally feel more comfortable thinking of addiction as a life experience that touches many of us but not all. An experience that for those who become ensnared offers a unique opportunity for choice and personal growth on a daily basis. I like the term 'recovery' because it implies a transitional state, with an end in sight but not yet reached. Rather than thinking of the condition as incurable, this allows me to focus ahead to a point of self-awareness which although may never be reached is nevertheless achievable.

Once we have experienced active addiction, our lives are never the same. On a deep level we understand what it is to be powerless over an external force, be it a substance or a behaviour, and we know that we have to be vigilant against the real enemy of recovery, our own minds. At this point many people find it a natural step to add spirituality into the mix. The 12-step programme, for example, encourages the belief in a power greater than ourselves which can act as a guide toward freedom from the destructive ego/mind that is obsessed with putting our own desires and fears above the needs of others.

When we make the first moves away from the active phase of addiction we are left with a priceless gift. Even if we go two steps forward and one step back for a while to come, we now have more hard-earned self-knowledge about who we are and what we are capable of than if we had never undertaken the journey in the first place.

This final section of the book is designed to help build on that self-knowledge, to help you recognize and go beyond the triggers and situations that you are bound to encounter and which are so dangerous to the progress you have made so far; to help you reach a point where you can recognize that you don't need to smoke dope or take drugs of any kind to get the most from your life or to enable you to experience authentic positive periods of inner peace and self-acceptance.

25. Regret – A Wasted Emotion

I was taught a long time ago that the two great wasted emotions are regret and guilt. They are often inter-connected, and both can be very dangerous to your recovery. Many of us emerge from the adjustment stage of withdrawal to find that the good feelings we are experiencing now we are free from our previous lifestyle are strangled by negative mind talk accusing us of not having quit earlier. Suddenly we see with clarity that the fear that held our dependency in place for so many years was to a large extent unfounded, and this gives our negative mind the perfect excuse to undermine our achievement.

Then there are those who start to think what life might have been if they hadn't picked up their first joint. What opportunities they have wasted or lost. The lovers who couldn't put up with their smoking. Times when they weren't fully engaged with their family. Regret about how they have treated other people who are no longer around for them to apologize to. These sorts of thoughts can lead to a really raw experience of deep self-loathing.

It would be easy for me to tell you not to indulge in these feelings, but once we are mired in them it's really hard to pull ourselves back out. I suggest that we can allow ourselves this indulgence just once and once only. We might allow this self-hate fest to last for a few hours, or at the very most one or two days; but after you have fully experienced the depth of your regret, I would ask you to make a conscious decision to put the worst of it away forever.

Afterward, you may decide to re-establish contact with someone, at a later date, either to let them see the new you or to apologize for previous behaviour. But this is not a step that should be taken lightly, or with an expectation of a particular outcome.

Indulgence sums up regret well. We get an unconscious payback from this sort of thinking. It's a short step away from self-pity, which is a state of mind that is familiar to many of us. Self-pity leads to paralysis. Brilliant! Before we know it we're back in the same state as we were when smoking – self-obsessed and stuck, unable to keep taking the positive steps that have moved us this far because our negative mind tells us we aren't worth it.

Regret and guilt act as blocks to new energy into our hearts, and therefore, logically, into our lives as well. Whilst we are living in the past, unable to change the things we feel most regretful about, we tend to ignore the brand new opportunities that are within our reach every day if only we could free our heads enough to explore them.

The solution

As soon as you find yourself drifting towards sad thoughts about what might have been, mentally make yourself stop by not letting the regret fantasies fully form in your mind. Instead, consciously start to create one or two *positive* fantasy thoughts. Think about your future, about the raw potential of every day. The possibility of a new job or new training, a new home, new relationships or friendships.

If you do find yourself beginning to get sucked into regret, try and pull yourself out by doing something grounded and practical that moves you forward into the future – researching new possibilities, for example, or contacting people who can help with your ambitions.

If life is difficult at this time, and it often is, rather than allowing yourself to sink into helplessness, commit to taking small steps that will begin to prove to those that care about you that you do have the strength to create lasting positive change under the most challenging circumstances.

26. Strengthening the Will

You do not have to look far to disprove the myth that all dope smokers are lazy. I have met many heavy dope smokers who are also highly driven to succeed. I was probably one of them myself, but in my case I also had a subconscious impulse to self-sabotage, which kept my aspirations pretty much in check. Ironically, I understood only too well at the time that my desire for success was driven to a large extent by fear of failure.

Plenty of people addicted to all sorts of things do manage to pull off the success trick, but often when they try and change their addictive behaviour, because it is destructive in other areas of life, they have difficulty maintaining the success momentum they have built up.

When we think about defeating addiction, or indeed becoming successful, many of us believe we need to use willpower to get us to the point where we can look back and feel a measure of security. There is a problem with this, however. Willpower, like drive, is all about using fear of failure to win our battles. Unfortunately, however driven we are, however much willpower we muster, it's possible to drive ourselves so hard that we seem to reach a point where we end up snapping because *"we've worked so hard. Surely we deserve a break?"*

Rather than coming from a place of fear, personal will can be summoned and strengthened by tapping into our own positive sense of self-worth. As a human being like any other, I can assure you I am in no position to lecture others about personal will; but over a period of time I have begun to understand that will, like so many other aspects of recovery, works best when it is built up slowly and nurtured with self-acknowledgement.

Like many addictive types, I am prone to making large, grandiose plans, but in retrospect I realize that all I needed to focus on during my first years of recovery was simply building the will to not smoke dope *today*. When I first quit smoking and was attending 12-step meetings, prayer was discussed. Though I personally did not find this difficult, I am aware that many people struggle with the concept of God and prayer. What worked for me was simply making the effort to kneel every morning. I saw it as symbolic. I wasn't praying to anybody, or anything in particular, I was just acknowledging that, by kneeling, today I was going to try not to be led by my ego. I would stay in this prayer position for perhaps a minute or two, sometimes just 20 or 30 seconds – as long as it took to get 'in the zone', to think good thoughts about someone other than myself, or get a sense of gratitude for what I had in my life.

I developed other rituals to perform before leaving the house in the morning, which revolved around meditation and exercise. Did any of this make me a better person? Quite honestly, probably not; certainly not in the short term. But I never missed a day. Even if I was really tired I made sure I got out of bed early enough to do what I had to do and still not be late for work.

Aside from the fact that a healthy morning routine was an excellent way of keeping my recovery moving in the right direction, I also noticed how good I felt after I had prayed, meditated or exercised, when part of me really didn't want to be bothered. I began to see that doing things I didn't want to do was a brilliant way of building up my personal (will)-power.

When we begin to understand that continuous choice is at the heart of dealing with cravings, it makes sense to recognize that building personal (will)power is also about making other positive life choices on a daily basis. In this way, it becomes easier to embrace life for what it is, rather than continually trying to distort or run away from everyday reality.

It helps to remember that many of us, from a really young age, became used to an extreme form of instant gratification, so re-learning by delaying gratification in other small ways is a sensible way to re-train our minds.

Perhaps it's as simple as just *doing the right thing*, both for ourselves and others. This can be quite an adjustment to make if we have always seen ourselves as unconventional or outsiders; but when we become less fearful and more loving, it doesn't mean we have to leave our free will at the door. My advice is to start with the small stuff, those things we instinctively tend to not notice or bother about. Whether it's listening to others without judging them, or helping out a neighbour or a friend, it's amazing how effective this sort of behaviour is in allowing us to feel good about ourselves again, and attracting positivity into our lives.

Some people in recovery get bitten by the bug and explore opportunities to volunteer to help others in their community. This can be especially useful as part of cognitive behavioural therapy for those prone to social anxiety or agoraphobia.

Of course, some people are addicted to overwork anyway, or have a martyr complex and would love the excuse to take on more and more tasks to add to their burden. If this is you, there is simply no point in exhausting yourself. The skill is recognizing the difference between driving yourself just to keep busy, and doing something that will give you real satisfaction. If you are a work addict, again this means learning how to operate through love rather than fear, all part of the process of not judging ourselves or others too harshly.

27. Monitoring our Moods

One anonymous Clearhead participant left their workbook behind at the end of the weekend. When I picked it up it seemed to be unused, but across a few pages at the back I found this wonderful choice of acronyms, which obviously summed up how he or she was feeling. So whoever you are, if you're reading this, thank-you.

Feel	F *ck
Emotion	Everything
And	And
Recover	Runaway

Nothing could sum up more neatly the choices we face on a daily basis during the process of recovery. Like food and alcohol, cannabis is all around us. Perhaps we live with people who are still smoking; maybe our neighbour likes a toke; and certainly we have friends and acquaintances who don't want to quit just because we have. We can't hide from cannabis. If we are addicted to dope the best we can do is accept that although we recognise how we might enjoy the first few smoking sessions, experience tells us that after a relatively short while we can find ourselves once again using it compulsively for limited pleasure.

As much as some people find that smoking dope exacerbated their depression, others maintain that it is when their cannabis self-prescription is taken away they find themselves starting to get the blues. Even after my own positive experience of quitting dope I went through a period of depression.

When we are stuck in our own negativity it's easy to wonder what's so great about feeling our emotions anyway. Surely life is just too difficult or painful? Doesn't everybody deserve the opportunity to numb out once in a while when it all gets too much? But does binge smoking or drinking to medicate our feelings change anything? Afterward the underlying emotional pain will still be there but will have an added dimension of self doubt.

Reflecting back on my own experience, I liken myself to a drowning man fleeing a shipwreck. After swimming for a while, finally I hit dry land. Filled with the euphoria of finding myself alive when I fully expected not to survive, I drink a little, eat a little and have a short rest; but as I recover my strength and look around my new environment, my heart sinks. I've landed on a desert island. I begin to realize that nothing is going to be easy. Surviving in the ocean was just the first step. Progressing from where I have landed is going to take much more effort than I bargained for.

If we have been smoking to run away from our problems, it's hardly surprising that when we finally have to face them they can seem daunting. Yes, there are things we can do on a practical basis to start making the necessary changes, but emotionally it's easy to feel dispirited or, in the short term, depressed.

Counselling and therapy

If your current life circumstances feel difficult to come to terms with, perhaps you might consider counselling. If this is something that you have shied away from for whatever reason, I recommend that you at least consider the possibility.

A good counsellor should be your guide, whether you seek to examine your past, to understand why you appear to continually make the same mistakes, or you need a witness to your current struggles so that you know you are not working alone.

The National Health Service can put you on the waiting list for a limited series of paid-for counselling sessions; or your locally run drug rehabilitation services should be able to offer you longer-term free or subsidized counselling to help you with your recovery.

If you can afford to pay for counselling then you have the opportunity to do some research before you approach someone. Counsellors specialize in different areas of practice, whether it's relationships, bereavement, addiction, or helping you deal with uncomfortable emotions, so it's important to decide which areas are your priority. If you are in recovery, you might not need to see an addiction specialist; it might be more valuable to gain insight as to why your recreational alcohol or drug use turned into dependency in the first place.

The usual procedure when choosing a counsellor is to arrange an initial consultation. From the counsellor's point of view, this will involve getting to know you and your history. There will probably be some form filling and general background questions. From your point of view, you should be looking carefully to see whether you think you can work with this person. You need to use your intuition to see if there is the potential for trust and growth in the relationship. At the end of the session, don't be concerned about telling the counsellor that you will contact him or her in a few days to let them know whether you want to proceed. And if there is no spark, you are entitled to thank them, pay them and not return. Counselling is an expensive service and it's better to write off the initial session than continue with someone who you feel is not going to be able to help you with your issues. I also think you should review your relationship with your counsellor every three months.

Of course it's true that this sort of work is going to encompass reflective times as well as breakthrough periods, but sometimes it can be a mistake to maintain the sessions beyond a point where they have ceased to be useful. When I quit smoking dope I allowed myself a treatment fund, which was about 50% more than I was spending on weed every month. After a year of seeing one particular counsellor, I changed tack and used the money for three months' worth of Shiatsu massage, which was wonderful in helping me release trapped emotion that couldn't be budged by talking therapy, although the work I had done in the counselling sessions had given me the insight to see where the problem lay in the first place.

It's hard for a layperson to make a distinction between counselling and psychotherapy. There is a considerable overlap and many similar skills are used; but psychotherapy is on the whole a longer process, often concentrating at the deepest level on childhood experiences to make sense of current issues.

Emotional literacy

Like many people, I can be vulnerable to anger outbursts when I am frustrated, or even when I have allowed myself to get hungry or overtired. I can become scared or panicky when I project too far into the future, or filled with self-doubt when I start to obsess about how I believe other people perceive me.

Whether you do or don't decide to go down the counselling or therapy route, you will certainly be dealing with real feelings and emotions on a daily basis. Wherever possible, make a point of noticing how you are feeling. Sometimes in quiet moments of reflection I mentally run through the day's occurrences – people I've interacted with, situations I've found myself in – and consciously think about how I felt at the time and what feelings I am left with now. Undertaking this little exercise for a minute or two even just once or twice a week helps me become more aware, generally, of how I am feeling at any given time, which in turn stops me from responding immediately from a reactive position.

28. Socializing in Recovery

Recovery from active addiction doesn't happen in a vacuum. Although it is true that as we learn to take responsibility for our own actions the only person we can ultimately ask questions of when we consider our choices is ourselves, we also have to recognize the role our friends and acquaintances play in cultivating and continuing a healthy lifestyle.

At the back of every dope smoker's mind when they consider the reality of their life without cannabis is the question of how they will manage those special intimate relationships that have been built up through years of shared stoned experience. In the early days of abstinence, most of us find it extremely difficult to be in situations where spliffs are being passed around. At the beginning, just meeting up with our smoking buddies, even when they are not smoking dope in front of us, can bring on strong feelings of association.

As the months pass and our resolve strengthens, we learn that, however hard we try, we can't avoid weed or the people in our lives who still smoke it; and so, slowly at first, we get used to being in situations where dope is available, in the same way as an alcoholic understands that his next drink is only as far away as the nearest bar.

It is also inevitable, however, that as we move forward we

find we are seeing less of those people to whom dope is still central in their lives – and this can be a bittersweet pill to swallow. On one hand we can feel horribly envious of our friends' easygoing attitude toward what we know from experience we have no control over, whilst on the other we are proud of our progress and our hard-won freedom from being dependent on weed ourselves.

As our minds clear and our recovery strengthens, most people find it easier to get a stronger feel for their own identity, to finally see who they really are when they strip away other people's expectations and judgements. This in itself allows moments of clarity when we think about our closest relationships. Taking this perspective, beyond using drink and drugs to drown our insecurities and screen out painful feelings, it might be useful for a moment to broadly classify ourselves and our friends as either hedonists or puritans.

In my experience, most people in recovery (from whatever addiction) still see themselves as hedonists who for reasons of health and safety can't sustain what can only be described as a self-destructive lifestyle. If we dig a little deeper, however, very often we find that we have taken on a little of the mindset of the puritan, to protect ourselves from the sad truth that we cannot indulge ourselves like our old friends seem to be able to.

Likewise hedonism can sometimes only have a limited shelf-life before it is spoilt by feelings of guilt and regret, which is why so often our friends are the first ones to ask us about quitting and how we did it. At Clearhead we often see what can only be described as a domino-like effect as friends of participants take stock of their own relationship with cannabis and often attempt to stop themselves, with varying degrees of success.

Meanwhile, when it comes to continuing our own recovery, we have to recognize that our smoking friends very often offer the first port of call when we make the decision to start smoking again. And let's be clear, smoking cannabis again, after a period of abstinence, for whatever reason is always an actual decision, even though very often it's made unconsciously, when sometimes – literally before we know it – we find a joint in our hand.

All we can do is continue to be honest with ourselves, so that we don't pretend to be surprised when we visit our dope-smoking friends and discover that, yes, weed is on offer if we want it, especially when we find ourselves just popping round to say hello when we are vulnerable to a lapse because of our mood.

The same goes for parties, gigs, or anywhere else where we know dope is going to be readily available. Rather than feigning surprise, the best policy is to prepare yourself mentally. If you do find yourself in this sort of situation, and know you don't want to smoke but are worried about the temptation, re-commit to abstinence; or if you do decide that this is the occasion to lapse, then read the next chapter.

29. Understanding Lapse and Relapse

People who have the wisdom of experience in the addiction field, whether recovering addicts themselves or drug workers, understand that lapse and relapse are part of recovery. A lapse can be described as a single episode; a re-lapse is where that single episode can trigger a regression back to where we are smoking as much as when cannabis was at its most negative, destructive or boring.

Why do lapses and relapses occur? Sometimes you could say that there is an intense build-up of pressure for the event; at other times it can be an unexpected opportunity, or we might see it as the answer to depression or disappointment, or even over-confidence in our ability to handle the odd smoke. But the overriding reason for going 'off-mission' is almost always rooted in conveniently forgetting the reality of our lives that led us to the point of wanting to stop in the first place.

If we slip in the early days, the experience can be physically unpleasant, just making us feel dizzy and sick. There can be other consequences as well; I remember smoking a pipe of neat weed once after a period of abstinence and suffering a terrifying panic attack on a crowded train.

But more often than not, a lapse simply reconnects the reward structures in our brain to create a pleasurable experience. Of course it does. These powerful systems might have been hardwired into place perhaps 10, 20, or even 30 years ago.

For a cannabis addict, that first smoke makes it appear as if the mind has slipped from its shackles, and suddenly we are capable of achieving whatever we want. Ideas and inspiration flood through us like they never went away, and our whole focus turns toward needing to keep the buzz going. And that's the clue. Notice how if you are sitting with other smokers you can barely wait for the joint to come your way again. Or if you are smoking by yourself, there is part of you that is already calculating how long the dope you have bought is going to last you, and when you are going to allow yourself to smoke again next time.

Very often we lapse or relapse when we travel, or when we return from travel. If opportunity arises whilst we are away, nobody there knows us and nobody at home needs to know our secrets. A friend of mine, a New Zealander, returned to her homeland from England and hooked up with her mates, some of which she hadn't seen for 10 years or more, when they all used to smoke together. She had been clean from cannabis here in London for two or three years but couldn't resist the temptation of smoking with her pals over a period of a week or two on holiday.

When she returned home, almost the first thing she did was get on the phone to a particular friend in London to score some weed just to *help* her through the jetlag. It was at this stage she saw what was happening, because on the plane home she had been resolute that her return to London would mark the end of her brief re-acquaintance with her old lover, the demon weed. So she made another call, this time to someone she knew she could talk honestly with, and who would remind her of her reasons for making her positive choices in the first place.

Ultimately, all I really can share is my own experience. At the beginning of every attempt to quit I was resolute, but the only significant amount of time I have ever gone without cannabis in my life is when I simply stopped smoking altogether. To do this I had to finally understand that I will never have any control over weed, and that I could either spend the rest of my life stoned, or obsessing about being stoned or I could change the way I lived, to take advantage of everything life has to offer from living with a clear head.

Afterword: Mad for it!

Skunk and the Law

Being UK-based, everything in this book is written from a British perspective; and it's impossible to write about cannabis use in Britain without considering the drug classification system and how it works to categorize illegal drugs in this country by their potential for harm using three distinct classes, which carry different legal penalties for possession and dealing.

Class A, the highest class, includes, as you might expect, heroin, cocaine, crack cocaine, as well as LSD.

For nearly 30 years cannabis was held in the secondary class B of illegal drugs, along with amphetamines and certain prescribed barbiturates.

Class C is reserved for various tranquilizers, as well as Ketamine and steroids.

During 2002, consistent pressure from the liberal left merged with new police thinking that arresting dope smokers was getting to be a waste of time, and raised the possibility that cannabis might be reclassified to the less dangerous C class, or even decriminalized completely.

In January 2004, after a trial run in the Brixton area of London, cannabis **was** finally reclassified from a B to a C class drug.

To offer some perspective, it is often forgotten that both ecstasy, the hugely popular recreational drug, and the use of psychedelic mushrooms, the organic tripper's drug of choice, are at the time of writing both in the most dangerous Class A bracket.

During the very early days of cannabis reclassification, the public and, perhaps more importantly from the Government's point of view, the media seemed to be generally in favour of a change that many sensed had been coming for some time. But after some months the mood began to change once more. Slowly at first, research started appearing in the media attempting to link cannabis use to serious damage to mental health; not all the research at this stage was conclusive, but respected psychiatrists and psychologists began to offer anecdotal evidence that the common link to more and more of the serious cases they were dealing with was a background of cannabis use.

The chorus of doubt grew louder, now joined by parents who were starting to write passionate articles in the newspapers about their own experiences within their families, of loved ones damaged to various degrees by cannabis-induced psychosis. At the same time, a new element was introduced into the debate – the prevalence of hydroponically grown strong skunk was seen by many opinion formers as the linking factor to the worst cases of cannabis psychosis.

Under pressure, Government commissioned a review of the decision, and in January 2006, exactly two years after the original reclassification, the Home Secretary Charles Clarke announced that he had been advised that the original decision was correct and should stand, but he was going to instigate a consistent and effective public health campaign to warn about the dangers of using the drug.

As if the situation weren't complex enough, militant dope smokers weren't letting the grass grow under their feet and began to petition the media with their own stories of how cannabis was offering real benefits, medicinally, for sufferers with ailments as diverse as multiple sclerosis, glaucoma and asthma, to name but three. The pressure was ratcheted up still further with regular reports in the press regarding violent criminals and murderers with long histories of cannabis abuse.

From 2006 until time of writing, the research linking cannabis to mental health damage has become more credible. With a change of political leadership, it seems possible, if not likely, that cannabis will be reclassified once more as a B or perhaps, goodness knows, even an A class dangerous substance.

Let's get real!

If you are British and have the slightest interest in cannabis and illegal drugs – and it seems that, for one reason or another, many people do – then none of the last few pages will be news to you. But is it possible, or even worth the effort, to pick the bones out of the various statistics, research and arguments, to make any sense of them? On the one hand, we have an influential and powerful selection of prohibitionists, including, it's fair to say, many distraught parents convinced that cannabis is fundamentally damaging. And on the other we have literally millions of users who believe passionately in their right to smoke cannabis because it gives them a great deal of pleasure, at **seemingly** only a relatively low risk to their health.

I started my work with Clearhead partly because it seemed that not enough is understood about cannabis dependency, and – certainly from my own experience and that of those I've tried to help – very little specialist help is available to anybody who has lost control over their dope smoking. So when people ask my position with regard to cannabis and the law, using the arguments surrounding the mental health issues, I find it simpler to keep my backside planted firmly on the fence. But nevertheless, I feel qualified to make some observations.

Firstly, having listened to many prohibitionists, their argument very often comes down to 'any loosening of the law concerning cannabis sends out the wrong message to young people'. In principle I agree, and yet if you imagine a spectrum of risk diversity with, at one end, kids who are entirely sensible and, at the other, kids who are in almost total rebellion, then in the middle you would find the largest proportion, those who are easily influenced. It seems to me that you could apportion the easily influenced kids evenly into those who will take a risk and those who won't; in other words, telling some people cannabis is dangerous will warn them off, and yet there are a whole set of others who, listening to the same message, will be spurred on out of rebellion or curiosity.

The fact is that most young people smoke dope the first time not because of peer pressure but because they are curious. The second and third time they smoke it, it's because they want to feel high; in other words, they like it. When the vast majority of them find that, far from making them crazy, smoking dope actually feels really nice, it's hard to win their trust back again – period.

Secondly, skunk is undeniably more potent than other forms of cannabis. It will turn your mind to mush much quicker than if you were smoking traditional strains of grass or hash. Day and night smoking of strong skunk over a period of years or even months will leave you with memory deficit and loss of brain function for years to come. It has a greater potential for addiction, partly because it ratchets up one's

THC tolerance, and partly because if you are smoking it with tobacco you use less of it and end up smoking more tobacco. If you are a young person smoking skunk, you will be damaging your young mind more profoundly than if you were smoking less potent types of cannabis. I would also imagine, although I'm not an expert in mental health, that skunk may trigger a psychotic episode quicker than normal weed or hash. However, the fact is that if you have the wrong genetic code, one or two tokes of the weakest hash joint could send you over the edge. I have worked with many people who avoid skunk if they can; plenty of others won't smoke anything else.

In 2007 a study was released, using pooled findings from around the world, that shows cannabis users are 40% more at risk from psychotic illness than non-users. However, these being statistics, it's a fair question to ask what the chances of a non-user developing a psychotic illness are in the first place. If, for example, the chance is 1%, then a 40% uplift to 1.4% is nothing to get very worried about; if, on the other hand, there is a 20% possibility, that is much more concerning. Statistics can of course work both ways. On the other side of the argument, the figures show that recorded use has actually decreased yearly in the period of reclassification. This could be because the police were arresting and cautioning fewer users; or one could say that word has filtered out and people have started listening to the warnings about the dangers of cannabis.

Lastly, this looks like being a debate that will go on for a long time. If the prohibitionists have their way, the frontline will surely turn to medicinal cannabis. We will see more and more cases of physically ill people, some of them pathetically so, stigmatized with a criminal record for using a drug that they believe is safer and helps relieve their symptoms better than anything they can get on prescription. The police will be obliged to spend a certain amount of time tied up dealing with Joe Stoner. Meanwhile, a percentage of people will suffer tragic consequences from their cannabis adventures; school kids will continue to smoke it anyway, because it feels good; and millions of others will smoke it compulsively even when it doesn't work for them any more, simply because they started so young they literally don't know how to stop.

Currently Clearhead are not running weekend work-shops.
Adrienne and I are in the process of expanding the work-shops into a new longer-term programme using some of the ideas in this book. We are also in the process of enhancing the Clearhead website so that people can support each other and self-monitor their cannabis use as they attempt to cut down or quit using cannabis altogether.

For further information, go to www.clearhead.org.uk

Clearhead Hypnotherapy Recording

with Angela Jullings

Cannabis and hypnotherapy

Almost all dependent cannabis smokers are conflicted over the drug. On the one hand, many still enjoy the feeling of being stoned but on the other can see that their dope smoking is causing a serious negative impact on many other areas of life, not least the fact that they have lost control over their use.

We have two minds – the conscious mind, which is our logical, thoughtful mind; and the unconscious mind, which is the mind responsible for all our behaviours, habits, beliefs and memories.

Hypnosis bypasses willpower, which belongs to the conscious mind, and can tap into what your unconscious truly feels about your cannabis smoking.

How does the Clearhead hypnotherapy recording work?

Track 1 Message from the author of this book, explaining a little more of his story and his relationship with cannabis, as well as giving you some idea of what to expect during your first days and weeks as the THC level in your body reduces.

Track 2 The first part of this track induces a light hypnotic trance, which is a very pleasant sensation of relaxation, somewhere between being asleep and awake. Using positive suggestion, the second part reinforces all of the reasons that you have for dealing with your dependence on cannabis. Many people find they actually fall asleep whilst listening to the recording, which is a real bonus for those suffering from a disrupted sleep pattern during the first few weeks after quitting. The positive messages are still absorbed by the unconscious mind even when asleep. The hypnotic messages last for a little over 30 minutes and are followed by a restful soundscape designed to encourage relaxation and undisturbed sleep.

Who can't use the recording?

If you have been diagnosed with epilepsy, or a psychiatric illness other than depression, please consult your doctor before using this product. Otherwise, the recording is safe for all ages.

The recording is designed for use at any time during the day or night, but **must not be used whilst driving, operating machinery, or in the bath.**

It is particularly effective if you have been using cannabis to help you sleep over a long period of time. It should be used in conjunction with any of the other ideas within the book that you think will be useful in restoring your natural sleep patterns. Remember that four hours' quality sleep without cannabis is worth eight when you're stoned.

The recording is available to purchase either as a digital download or in compact disc format from www.clearhead.org.uk

Your hypnotherapist: Angela Jullings

Angela is an experienced hypnotherapist and psycho-therapist. She has an instinctive ability to help people lose the negative habits and controlling thoughts that keep them trapped, and replace them with their own natural underlying desire for positive change. She has operated her own practice since 1995, and has a lifelong interest in people and their behaviour. Clients frequently come to Angela wanting to stop smoking cigarettes; or they might be seeking help with depression, panic attacks, or an inability to relax or sleep properly. Angela began to see that sometimes the underlying problem stopping her clients helping themselves with these issues was an unspoken dependence on cannabis.

Her wide-ranging experience in the fields of personal development, hypnotherapy and psychotherapy has made her one of today's outstanding therapists. Her extensive training over the years has earned her diplomas in advanced therapeutic hypnosis, psychotherapy. She is also a Neuro Linguistic Programming master and trainer.

Angela is registered with the National Council for Hypno-therapy, is a senior member of the General Hypnotherapy Register, and is registered with the BACP.

Angela can be contacted through her website:
www.angelajullings.com

© Angela Jullings 2008

Breaking Your
Cannabis
Dependence

hypnotherapy recording

With Angela Jullings in association with Clearhead
Music by David Plotel

If you have brought this book from a store or from an online bookseller and wish to purchase the recording from our website at the discounted package price you will need to email the code H7c297A3 using the *offer@hindsightpress.com* button.

Resource Section

Clearhead

www.clearhead.org.uk
www.clearheadonline.com

The Twelve Step fellowships

Marijuana Anonymous (International)
www.marijuana-anonymous.org.uk

Marijuana Anonymous
UK Helpline 07940 503438

Narcotics Anonymous (International)
www.na.org

Narcotics Anonymous – United Kingdom
www.ukna.org

Alcoholics Anonymous (International)
www.alcoholics-anonymous.org

Alcoholics Anonymous – United Kingdom
www.alcoholics-anonymous.org.uk

Nicotine Anonymous (International)
www.nicotine-anonymous.org

Co-dependency Coda
www.codependents.org (International)

Co-dependency Coda – United Kingdom
www.coda-uk.org

Cocaine Anonymous
www.ca.org (International)

Cocaine Anonymous – United Kingdom
www.cauk.org.uk

Families Anonymous (International)
www.families-anonymous.org

Families Anonymous – United Kingdom
www.famon.org.uk

Debtors Anonymous (International)
www.debtorsanonymous.org

Debtors Anonymous – United Kingdom
www.debtorsanonymous.org.uk

Activity and self-help resources

Laughter

www.laughteryoga.org (International)

www.laughternetwork.co.uk United Kingdom

Personal Development

www.moretolife.org (International)

www.osho.leela.co.uk (United Kingdom)

www.aummeditation.com (London)

Seeking a Therapist

British Association for counseling Psychotherapy

www.bacp.co.uk

(United Kingdom)

Volunteering

www.guerillagardening.org (International)

www.csv.org.uk (International)

www.capitalvolunteering.co.uk (London)

Meditation Buddhist

Vipassana 10-day silent retreats

www.ubakhin.com (International)

Mindfulness-Based Cognitive Therapy MBCT

www.lbc.org.uk/breathingspacecourses (London)

Yoga and Meditation Hindu

www.sivananda.org (International)

www.sivananda.co.uk (United Kingdom)

Christian Retreat Centre

www.penhurst.org.uk (United Kingdom)

Alternative therapies to help adjustment process

Acupuncture

www.acupuncture.org.uk (United Kingdom)

Emotional Freedom Technique

www.energy-therapydirect.co.uk (South East England)

Hypnotherapy

www.angelajullings.com

(London Consultations / Recordings International)

Improving your memory in recovery

Dr Kawashima's Brain Training Nintendo Computer Game

Recommended reads

Addictive Thinking. Abraham J. Twerski
ISBN 1568381387
Published in the United Kingdom by Hazelden

Wise Highs: How to Thrill, Chill, and Get Away from it All Without Alcohol or Other Drugs. Alex J. Packer
ISBN 1575421984
Published in the United States by Free Spirit Publishing

The Power of Now. Eckhart Tolle
ISBN 0340898917
Published in the United Kingdom by Hodder & Stoughton

How to Stop Smoking and Stay Stopped for Good. Gillian Riley
ISBN 0091917034
Published in the United Kingdom by Vermilion (Random House)

Healing Anxiety with Herbs. Harold H. Bloomfield
ISBN 072253694172
Published in the United Kingdom by Harper Collins

Say Good Night to Insomnia. Gregg D. Jacobs
ISBN 0805055487
Published in the United States by Owl Books

Beating Anger: The Eight-point Plan for Coping with Rage. Mike Fisher

ISBN 1844135640

Published in the United Kingdom by Rider

Free Yourself from Fear. Lucy Atcheson

ISBN 1401915817

Published in the United Kingdom by Hay House

Psychiatric Drugs Explained. David Healy

ISBN 0443074143

Published in the United Kingdom by Churchill Livingstone